OUT OF TIME

OUT OF TIME

James Fountain

Book Guild Publishing
Sussex, England

First published in Great Britain in 2006 by
The Book Guild Ltd
25 High Street
Lewes, East Sussex
BN7 2LU

Typesetting in Times by
Acorn Bookwork Ltd, Salisbury, Wiltshire

Printed in Great Britain by
Antony Rowe Ltd, Chippenham, Wiltshire

A catalogue record for this book is available from
The British Library.

ISBN 1 85776 958 9

Special thanks to Johanes Prastomo,
Harry Watson, Blake Morrison,
Richard Beard and Hannah Griffiths

To my wonderful family and friends, who
constantly inspire possibility.

1

I went into my room, the cream walls, pastel green curtains
and carpet were colours that seemed to mark a safe retreat. I
gazed with fresh eyes upon the tartan quilt across my bed, then
lay on it, my eyes upon the ceiling. My feet shaking, I recalled
the night's events cinematically in my mind, and found them
faintly amusing. A rush through my abdominal muscles as if I
was experiencing an orgasm took my thoughts away from
Rachel. Her very name seemed unfamiliar now, drifting into
the stratosphere. My head and my whole body felt light and
elastic, as though I'd just done warm-up exercises for a
hundred-metre sprint. I was completely alert.

As I looked in a mirror I saw pupils the size of buttons, my
eyes far larger than they usually were. Thoughts were
becoming transitory, difficult to hold on to and follow
through. Rationalising now seemed beyond me as I lay there,
eyes screwed up, remembering now only fragments of the
evening, as the original cinematic reel fell off the projector and
shattered on the floor.

My eyes searched the room as if they belonged to a new-
born baby. Everything was new, everything was fascinating.
The green disc-shaped wall-lights, the green curtains, the green
carpet. Why all this green? The cream walls, the wooden desk
covered in papers, the wooden bookcase. I walked over to the
bookcase and read the titles, picking out random volumes and
looking at them with interest. I found myself looking at the
publisher's details as opposed to the book itself. I wanted to
know where everything came *from*. How was I connected to all
of this? My identity was in question. I began to lose touch with
who I was.

I had no need of sleep. I discovered an A4 pad on my desk,

found a pen, and looked about me. My sight became transfixed by a rugby poster across from me as I sat on the bed. 'ENGLAND' – its bold white capital letters jumping out and slapping me in the face.

I gathered together an A4 pad, my notebook and a dictionary. I looked up 'England' in the dictionary. *The largest division of the British Isles, conquered in 1066 in the Norman invasion* ... This failed to fit my own interpretation of the word's meaning, and so I invented my own, and wrote it on the pad.

ENGLAND – ONE LAND

I gave way to stream of conscious thought, transcribing things to paper the moment I thought of them. I was at the centre of a brainstorm, and the eventual results would have groundbreaking impact on the world at large.

5 CONTINENTS
7 SEAS
9 PLANETS
A SOLAR SYSTEM
AT ITS CENTRE – (?)

EUROPE – WORLD CENTRE FOR DRIVE, IMAGINATION, LITERATURE, INDIVIDUALITY, CREATIVITY

YARM SCHOOL – FOR THE DEVELOPMENT OF TOP INTELLECTUALS, FUTURE WORLD LEADERS

HEADMASTER – MEMBER OF 60 HEADMASTERS, A BOARD FOR BRITAIN

EUROVISION – HOW DO THEY DO THAT(?)

12 DISCIPLES:
James
John
Mark
Luke
Christopher
David
George
Paul
Nicholas
Peter
Daniel
Bartholomew

INSTILLED IN SOCIETY THROUGH EACH AGE,
MANIFESTATIONS OF HUMAN LIFE THOUGHT
NECESSARY BY ⑦

I wrote hurriedly, fearing that if I did not write down my
ideas immediately they would be lost forever. This was an
explanation, an equation for life itself. Whilst I wrote I heard
voices that seemed to be coming from above me, gradually
merging into what sounded like a hymn being sung by a
church choir. The sound seemed appropriate to what I was
doing, the seal of approval from God. It seemed I was a
biblical prophet who had been presented with a vision from the
Almighty. Occasionally I would look up from my labour to see
shadows shrinking away into the corners of the room, as it
began to be filled with light. I foresaw evil being drawn out of
society through my writings, and the shadows shrunk away as
screams of anguish and pain filled my ears. As light replaced
these shadows I heard joyful sounds of laughter and relief.

Was I a saint? Was I one of the 12 disciples manifested
throughout the generations of man? Had I been recalled to the
world by God to gather for the Second Coming? Suddenly
conscious of a great fear, I wrote:

THIS IS DANGEROUS. BE CAREFUL. LIFE WILL
NEVER BE THE SAME⊘

In spite of my fear, I felt compelled to continue. I turned to
the notebook and scribbled a word or a phrase on each of the
remaining pages, in large, frantic capital letters.

SOMERSET HOUSE
GO TO THE MOUNTAINS – SEE THE WORLD
FROM ON HIGH
EUROVISION
9 PLANETS
7 SEAS
5 CONTINENTS
3 FORMS – COMMERCE, INDUSTRY AND
IMAGINATION
ENGLAND – 'ONE LAND'
YALE + YARM = OXFORD
EMILY BRONTE – FIND HER ON THE MOORS
THREE FORMS. ONE⊘

I picked up novels around me that I had written in past lives.
The words in them seemed so familiar that I felt I must have
written them. I started to believe that I was once my grandfather, Dr James Richard Fountain, and that I had been
reborn as James Richard Thomas Fountain.

Ideas constantly flowed and shaped in my mind. I looked at
the Time Cube clock by my bedside, and as I watched the
digits changing I heard a car go past the window at precise five
minute intervals – five past, ten past, quarter past, and so on.
This meant time had a meaning, that God was giving me
another clue, another sign. This must mean Creation had
lasted only an hour, and not six days with a day of rest. Each
of the 12 disciples had played a five-minute role in the world's
make-up, given overall instruction from God. The passing of
each car that I heard represented the splitting up of each stage,

and brought in the next disciple. From this point I came rapidly to the conclusion that God was now recalling his disciples for use in the modern age.

If I died I would be reincarnated to start again, with the same set of principles intact in my soul. This would apply to the rest of the disciples, so that there would be 12 representatives of God continually reincarnated in order to safeguard mankind.

I envisaged great celebration at my discoveries, large meetings of world powers at which I would be guest of honour. The whole world was watching as I wrote and thought at these moments. Life was being pulled up to a higher plane, and I was God's communicative instrument.

I now turned to the question of who to deliver this vital information to. My message would be spread more quickly if I told the higher authorities first. I decided upon London as the most sensible place to go. I would go to Downing Street and speak directly with the Prime Minister. After that I would leave for Brussels to speak with the President of the European Union, followed by meetings with the Secretary General of the United Nations, and the President of the United States. The world must know.

All this must be completed within a week. My school skiing trip next Saturday would allow me to get to the mountains, to see the world on high, a vital insight from my brainstorm. God would be waiting for me in the Alps with further instructions and the aid of a greater plane of view. I reached for my rucksack.

The time was approaching seven o'clock as I gathered together all I thought necessary. I decided it was best to travel light, to pack only those things of basic necessity. A five pound note, bank card, A4 pad, toiletries, address book, Walkman, Shakespeare, Coleridge, Emily Bronte's *Wuthering Heights*, some poetry books that I had been writing in since I was a child, and a Bible.

I paused for a moment and listened. My parents had not yet risen. I thought of sneaking away quickly to the train station. It was only a half-hour walk. I didn't want to meet any opposition from anyone. If I left a message, they would surely understand.

A thud from the next room cancelled this out as a possibility. I could not leave without telling them first.

My eyes were drawn to the Time Cube once more. I held it for a few moments, the clock displaying 7:09. As I placed it down the digits changed to 7:10 the second it left my hand. I tried it again, and again the digit altered at the precise moment of my release. The whole world was suspended, out of time, as I held the clock. My excitement fizzed over. I rushed into my parents' room like a child on Christmas morning, holding the Time Cube triumphantly in my right hand. My mother and father looked aghast.

'I've done it!' I said excitedly.

'Done what?' my mother asked.

'I've stopped time!' I yelled, disbelief quickly writing itself over my parents' faces. 'Look, when I hold this clock, time stands still. When I release it the digits move, and time starts again!'

I felt they needed convincing and, noticing the tea tray and steaming teapot, I poured my mother and father diplomatic cups of tea. But as I turned to pass them over the bed, I realised they were beyond diplomacy. My mother looked as though she was about to cry, her face paling, her dark eyes concerned. My father more puzzled than I had ever seen him, his grey eyebrows twitching. He had put down the crime novel he was reading. It was time to leave. I saw my mother reach for the telephone as I closed the bedroom door behind me.

I pulled the battery out of the Time Cube. From now on, everything I did would be out of time, and the world would hang suspended. I would thus have plenty of time to do what I needed before going to the Alps. I put on my jacket and zipped up my bag. I stared myself down in the mirror, my eyes clear and bright, convinced this was the right thing to do. I headed down the corridor and my mother shocked me by turning into the corridor at the same moment. She was fully dressed.

'Oh! Where are you off to at this time in the morning, James?'

'London.'

'Well you're not, you're coming with me. I'm going to take you to see somebody,' she said matter-of-factly.

'Who?'

'A man who will help you,'

'Excellent.'

My mother showed surprise as I followed immediately behind her. I was sure she'd guessed my master plan, realised the importance of it and begun to help spread my message. This was obvious because she took me straight out in the car without any breakfast. It would have to be important for my mother to not mind me missing breakfast. I followed her to the car, my bag slung over my shoulder, my jacket still on.

Soon it became clear that it was not the parish church that my mother was taking me to, but Hartlepool General Hospital. She began to speak to me slowly and lucidly as though I were a child, saying nothing which invited a reply. I was becoming confused.

'Now listen, James, I'm taking you to see someone who will help you. He thinks he knows what is wrong with you, but you must do as he says, alright? Good lad.'

She emphasised the 'good' as though I were in searing pain, like she had when I'd closed a penknife on my finger ten years before.

We pulled into the hospital car-park and found a space. I followed my mother out of the car, and entered the hospital. A nurse in her thirties wearing a light blue uniform appeared to be waiting for us. She eyed me circumspectly, then turned to my mother.

7

'Mrs Fountain?' she inquired, in a crisp, sterile voice.

'Yes.'

'Can you and your son follow me, please?'

The nurse led us through the accident and emergency ward and into a cubicle, drawing the blue curtain around it. The nurse regarded me for an instant through small grey eyes. My mother sat in one of the three plastic seats. I remained standing, preparing to run through the ward and escape to the station. An elderly Indian doctor entered at that moment.

'Could you sit down please?' he commanded, his deep, aged voice encouraging me to postpone my mission. I sat.

'Thank you. Now, could you tell me how you feel at this particular moment in time, James?'

'I'm great. But I need to pass on a communication from God, and am anxious to get on and tell the world's leaders about it. I received a vision last night.'

'Vision? What kind of vision?' The doctor adjusted his spectacles.

'Well, ideas in my head mostly, though I did hear voices when the evil shrank away into the corners of my room leaving only the goodness behind.'

I expected rapturous applause from hospital staff, tears of joy, hugs all round. The doctor struggled to clear his throat and left the cubicle without saying another word. My mother suddenly rose and followed him. I felt the restriction of the sterile cubicle. I saw my chance. I ran. Through A & E. Through the automatic door. Into the car park. I'd done it. I looked about me, stared at the road I would have to cross then head down in order to reach the station. Hesitating, I heard running footsteps close behind me, and was rugby tackled on the grassy area just outside the hospital grounds. The grey eyes of a nurse smiled into my own surprised eyes, my shins pinging with pain from her muscular tackle. The ever-ready women of Hartlepool.

'Where did you think you were going, then?' she grinned,

gathering her breath and clasping my arm.

I was taken to where my mother was sitting at a pay phone, her eyes upon me, now tinged with anxiety. The nurse left me in close proximity, then walked away. My mother spoke as quietly as she could, though I could hear every word.

'He's just not right, Beryl. He told the doctor he'd seen a vision last night, that he heard voices ... I don't know ... they're going to tell me soon ... no, Beryl ... oh, alright – James! Come and speak to your Aunty Beryl.' She handed me the phone.

'Hi, James, are you alright?' my aunt asked.

'The future of the world depends upon my deliverance of God's message but for some reason I'm being held here. I'm hoping to be released soon.'

'Oh.'

'I don't expect you and my mother to fully understand. But I *must* go. Take care.'

'You too.' I handed the phone back to my mother.

Confusion. I was 'not right' apparently. Clearly my mother did not understand. My Aunty Beryl didn't seem convinced. And she was a church-goer.

As I re-entered the ward with my mother, a large middle-aged man in plain clothes and modern, narrow-framed spectacles approached me. He led me to a room, asked my mother to wait in the corridor, and bid me sit. He sat in the chair opposite as I faced the single window. A hospital bed and equipment lay behind him. A small green light shone like an emerald from a piece of equipment.

'Now then, James, could you start by explaining to me exactly what happened last night, please?' He spoke in a tired, world-weary way. Perhaps he had a hangover.

'I went to Hardwick Hall, to an organised event with friends. My friend Julian and I went for a walk in the woods, and we talked about the future ...'

'And what happened when you got home?'

9

'I began to see shadows moving into the corners of my room and disappearing, being replaced with light ...' I smiled and hesitated. A shaft of sunlight suddenly poured through the window, from a bright early February sky. God approved.

'Go on, please.' the man said, becoming impatient.

'Yes, the shadows disappeared, and as they did I heard screams of pain from the evil being taken out of the world, and the joyous laughter of the good that replaced it.'

The man did not reply. He seemed to be making careful notes on a red clipboard. Then he stood up suddenly, moved to the door, paused and was gone.

I was alone for some time. I eyed the green light nervously. Our conversation was being recorded. I was being tested, as a superbeing, a visionary. Scientists wanted to know what made me tick. That was why I had been brought here. I should have guessed earlier.

Clinically clean white walls. That antiseptic smell. I hated hospitals. I walked towards the window, which looked out on to the nearby roundabout and petrol station. I was a prisoner. People did not buy what I said. Instead of lapping it up, these doubters and rationalisers were trying to dissect what I was saying, communicate with God themselves, rather than take the message first-hand. Why wouldn't they listen? I tilted my head to the blue, closed my eyes as the sun warmed my face. I lifted my arms.

The door banged suddenly and I turned with a jump.

'Would you move away from the window, please?' the man with modern, narrow spectacles demanded. I sat down once more. 'There's a few more questions I need to ask you.'

'OK.' I now suspected he was a police officer, his tone of voice reminding me of Morse or Taggart. Had I committed a crime?

'Now then, did you drink any alcohol last night?'

'Yes, I drank a couple of pints of cider.'

'Is that all?'

'Yes.'

'Anything else?'

'Er, yes, a glass of lemonade at the beginning of the night.'

'OK. Did you take any drugs last night, James?'

'No. I never have.'

'Right. Wait here one moment.'

He disappeared again, but this time he was away only briefly. He soon re-entered, clutching my bag.

'Now,' he said, sitting himself down, 'can you tell me what is in this bag?'

'Basic things – washing things, money, cash card, Shakespeare ...'

He cut in: 'Just tip the things out on the floor and show me will you?' The man raised his voice, again impatient.

I tipped the bag upside down, and the belongings I had intended to take along with me to London, Brussels and Washington DC, to aid me in my Divine quest tumbled onto the floor like a child's toys. The man searched carefully among them, tipped out my wash-bag, and checked the rucksack, making sure it was empty. And then he drifted out of the room once more.

I gazed through the window, the sunlight creeping out from behind a cloud, angelic choral music filling the room. It was the same as the sound I had heard as I sat on my bed earlier in the morning.

Suddenly the door banged and my mother was beside me sobbing incessantly, her cheeks wet with tears. She said nothing, just pressed my head towards her shoulder and hugged me tightly. Finally she spoke.

'The doctors want to keep you here for a little while.'

'Why?'

'We don't know yet. Just get plenty of rest. We'll be visiting you every day, son, so you won't be too lonely.'

What was she talking about? Why was she crying? I needed to get to the station. I needed to get to London. Nobody was

11

listening to me. I felt the frustration of the child that is misunderstood, that does not have the vocabulary to make his needs clear to the outside world.

The large man with the narrow glasses now stepped into the room wearing a long white medical jacket. He spoke more cautiously now that my mother was in the room.

'There now. If you'll just come this way please.' He was talking to me.

'What about my things?' I looked at them, lying dumbly upon the floor. They embarrassed me somehow, I felt I was being dissected.

'Oh, don't worry about them,' my mother said, 'I'll pick out a few things for you and bring them to you tonight.'

'Thanks. Bye.' I left my mother without ceremony, confused at my proposed confinement, and as she began to walk away there came a fresh burst of tears and sobbing.

We walked down a long disinfected corridor until we reached an industrial, rustic-looking elevator. I noticed the man now wore a name tag which read 'Dr Rogers' in small type. He pressed button number two as we entered the elevator, and seconds later, the lift doors opened. I stepped out into a hospital ward that was unlike any I had ever been in. This was no accident and emergency room. All patients were mobile, as I spotted some moving around in the corridor unassisted by nurses. I heard the sound of pool balls clicking nearby. The walls were decorated in floral designs, not whitewashed. The floor was carpeted, rather than hard and polished.

Dr Rogers directed me to an office and left me. I was now in the company of a woman in her late fifties with a shock of dyed brown permed hair and a few greyish hairs around her ears. She fixed me with her eyes, a stunning sky-blue.

'Could I take your name please, son?' she asked, in a thick Hartlepudlian accent.

'James Fountain.'

'Any middle names?'

'Richard Thomas.'

She fed the results of her questioning into a computer, taking also my date of birth, home telephone contact details, address and next of kin. I noticed the wonderful view through the window to my left. Hills towered up and became farmland and flowery meadows, wooded areas in between. And yet I was certain this was the location of a large housing estate. The great Change had taken place. The events of last night, my discoveries, had altered the landscape, taken the countryside back some 50 years. The world was resolving itself ...

'Next of kin! Next of kin! Mr Fountain, I'm afraid you'll have to give me your details as I ask you for them.' She was annoyed. I came back from my euphoria momentarily.

'Yes, I'm sorry. I was just admiring your wonderful view.'

'What wonderful view? I'm sorry Mr Fountain, I would like you to stick to answering my questions. I've no idea what you're talking about.'

I did as she said. She was obviously having a bad day. Possibly she was disgruntled at having to work on Sundays at her age.

Presently Dr Rogers came to collect me from the miserable blue-eyed administrator. He led me to a more medically-themed room, and asked me to roll up one blue and white sleeve. For the first time I realised I had not changed my clothes since the previous night. The doctor took some blood with a syringe stab that felt like a paper cut, then wrote an address which included 'Liverpool', sealed the sample inside it and placed it on the desk.

I was given a guided tour of the ward, shown some activities I might like to try to pass the time: the pool table, the television, the magazines. These were all situated in the large living-room, the first room on my right as I walked up the corridor. All other rooms contained beds or toilets. There were two toilets, one at either end of a long, wide corridor. None of the staff pointed out to me wore name tags or a uniform. By now I had lost track of why I was here. Did I work here? Was this my new job?

As we slowly walked along the corridor I gazed through windows that looked into the rooms and saw people lying in bed, tossing and turning or reading newspapers. Nobody appeared to notice me looking. An old man hobbled down the corridor, his eyes frantic and bewildered. Dr Rogers paused for a moment to take him back into his room.

Eventually we were there.

'This will be your room. Yours is the first bed on the left. If you want to use the loo, check with the nurse across the corridor first,' the doctor stated. And then he left me, whistling some mundane tune as he disappeared down the corridor.

2

I sat for some time upon my allotted bed, trying to take in my surroundings. There were six beds in the large, bright room. The walls were white, the floor a light shade of tan, sun pouring through the panoramic window across to my left. Two small windows looked out on to the corridor, one of which was beside my bed. Through this window a man in his mid-thirties with slicked black hair and pale complexion seemed to have fixed a constant blank stare upon me. He sat leisurely in a chair, his feet upon the desk in front of him.

I noticed I was alone in the room, except for one man in the bed furthest from me, beside the panoramic window. He lay with his knees up and his eyes closed, making a small wigwam out of the covers. I rose and looked more closely at his face. He had long brown hair and a beard. Could it be? Was it Jesus? My heart missed a beat and I froze. But it all made sense. Jesus needed to talk with me personally before I embarked on my mission. He was just resting up after an exhausting descent from Heaven.

I gawped at the Messiah in dumb wonder for several minutes. Then my attention was grabbed by a newspaper that lay on the table beside Him. The headline screamed from its front page.

YOU HAVE WON ONE MILLION POUNDS

It was a test. Jesus wanted to know if I would prefer personal wealth over the welfare of the world. The money was there for me if I wanted it. All I had to do was pick up the paper and someone would come and congratulate me and whisk me away by helicopter to some exotic location for a grand presentation ceremony to mark my achievements. But I would not be tempted. I was unflinching in my faith. I was an example to all men.

Each of the six beds within the room had a wardrobe beside it. These were wooden, the same light beige colour as the flooring, and on wheels. Each of the four other sections were individually decorated, evidently according to the taste of each occupant. One was wallpapered purple and blue, and when I opened the wardrobe I saw an array of glittering, bright fabrics hung up. The air smelt of incense and perfumery here. Next to this was a section draped in sports posters; rugby, football and cricket. Its wardrobe was filled with tracksuits, T-shirts, jeans and some modern night-clubbing gear. A further section had a natural theme. A large tree shape cut out of dark green felt adorned the wall space over the bed and pictures of birds and other wildlife were dotted around. The clothes in the wardrobe were rugged and hard-wearing – corduroy trousers and woolly jumpers. The final section was dark and gothic – black wallpaper, Velvet Underground memorabilia, a clock ticking irritatingly from the bedside table. Black clothing made up the majority of the wardrobe.

Finally I stood back and considered. This was another test. My stay here was a test of identity. These four sections were an outward projection of my personality. There was the purple and blue section, which would belong to my ideal woman, all bright fabrics and exotic perfumery. The sport section showed my sporting interest, as both player and spectator. The naturalist section displayed my interest in ornithology and the natural world in general. And finally there was my dark side, a fascination with death, and music which closely regards melancholia and treads a fine line between life and death. These were the four main phases I had been through in my life and aspects that remained with me. I recognised that I was now treading the fourth of these phases, that fine line between life and death, searching for the pins that held all together.

I stepped towards the plain section. A white file was hinged upon the wardrobe to the right of the bed, and I sat down and rummaged through the contents. A pen, a few printed A4 sheets and a sealed envelope fell out. Amongst the print were fire safety regulations and information regarding patient visiting hours, each of which had the Hartlepool and District Health Authority logo at the top. I opened the envelope, which was unaddressed. It read as follows.

THE INDEPENDENT PEOPLE'S TRUST

Dear Sir,

The Independent People's Trust would like to inform you that we would value any comments you have regarding the running of this hospital ward, and whether or not this could be improved. If you come up with any ideas or suggestions, we would like to meet you on 3 March 1996 to discuss these points.

Yours sincerely

J. D. Eastwood

E. Westmoreland

I had been placed here as a troubleshooter, to test-run the ward for faults, to iron out problems. Eastwood and Westmoreland: east meeting west. More clues. I knew it was all a code for something larger-scale. It was a message that told me to continue the good progress I had already made, that as I did so east would continue to meet west, and ends would continue to be met. By 3 March the world would be complete and I would meet the two key representatives for freedom –

Eastwood and Westmoreland – the east of the past and the west of the future. Poor and rich nations alike were now moving toward peace and stability.

I walked over to the panoramic window and took in the view. At first I noticed nothing remarkable. In front of me was a dual carriageway, and beyond that to my right lay the hilly wooded areas I saw from the administrator's window. Cars swished to and fro on the road. And yet, as I looked more closely I realised the landscape to my left was being altered. The green hillside appeared to be swallowing up the housing estate. A blurred patch moved steadily from the left, as housing was replaced by green hillside, then a large field formed. As I watched in astonishment the cars in front of me were also changing. When I had first looked there were the usual array of modern Fords, Vauxhalls, Volvos, Jaguars, Skodas and so on. But suddenly the *age* of the cars began to change. I saw a pattern develop – a black car would be followed by a white car followed by another black car, and then they came in threes – three black, three white, three black. The cars which came next were makes of the 1940s and 50s, such as old Jags, Triumphs and Rovers. The cars were changing along with the landscape. The world had been moving along too quickly. Time was going into reverse.

I ran to my bed and picked up a pen and a sheet of paper. This must be recorded. As I moved back to the window I was surprised to realise the cars of yesteryear had suddenly been replaced by modern cars. Yet as I watched, the same transformation took place as before, this time with a system of a red car followed by a white followed by a red, then three red, three white, and three red. And once more the older models completely dominated the road. I was incredulous, wide-eyed in wonder. It had worked. The Golden Age was returning, as the world improved. Yet I found myself considering other possibilities – that I was God, that this was my creation, that I wanted to see classic rather than modern

18

cars, hills and fields rather than houses, that this was done because *I* wanted it done. That *I* created the world.

I wrote on the back of the fire regulations sheet, resting upon the windowsill. I saw numberplates that contained coded messages. I pondered who they could be from. YCN – You Can Now. SNL – Son Now Lives. That was it. I was the Son of God. And yet Jesus lay behind me, sleeping as I watched. Perhaps I had been allocated for the task of world improvement, maybe God wanted the landscape of my mind to be reflected in the landscape of the earth. The numberplate: F478 CWR evidently stood for 'Christ Will Return'. God was relaying messages back to me in a code that I alone understood. Each numberplate that I discovered to be of significance was scribbled down hurriedly on the paper.

The colour sequences now took on a further significance. The following system of coding for three cars in succession was indicative of the professions of the drivers of those vehicles.

Blue, green, black – executive/businessman
Red, white, red – doctor/nurse
Black, white, black – creative/designer/artist/writer

I worked for some time and deciphered a number of these sequences, all of which I wrote down for future reference. I saw a series of patterns that must be resolved in my own mind in order for east to continue to meet west. My energy level soared. Not a slight feeling of tiredness had crept behind my eyes, though I had now been awake for more than 26 hours. It was just after noon. I had been stood writing at the window for over two hours.

I kept going. Had to keep going. Rather than processing and distilling my thoughts before I wrote, I reverted to the stream of conscious method I had applied many hours previous. Everything in front of me was symbolic in some way, like a Pre-Raphaelite painting. I tried to take it all in, the visibly shifting landscape, east meeting west, time rolling back, myself in between.

EASTWOOD – WESTMORELAND
MERGING INTO ONE SIDE
MANKIND FILTERING OUT THE BAD
THREE FORMS OF LIFE
COMMERCE * IMAGINATION * INDUSTRY
INDUSTRY IS DRIVEN BY IMAGINATION
COMMERCE SPREADS THE WORD
EASTWOOD – IMAGINATION
WESTMORELAND – WORLD OF THE FUTURE
METROPOLIS – FUTURE OF CIVILISATION
THE LINK WITH EUROPE
CHRIST WILL RETURN
(?) WILL SEND HIM BACK
THE LINK HAS BEEN MADE
FOUNTAIN OF YOUTH
THE ETERNAL FOUNTAIN
PLOUGH IN THE FIELDS
SOWING THE SEEDS
DOVES FLYING BEHIND

The final three lines were written as I noticed a tractor beginning to plough the field that had just taken the place of a housing estate, with white doves flying behind. Peace, hope, prosperity. They were symbols of goodwill for the Golden Age. It was time for tranquillity.

The lane along which cars drove in order to exit the dual carriageway was a kind of conveyor belt filtering away evil. The dual carriage, itself blurred now, was being replaced by a single road. A workman wearing a yellow hard hat and blue overalls carried a sign and fixed it up on the opposite side of the road so that it faced me, and squinting I could make out the lettering, which I wrote down.

SHERLOCK HOMES – GATEWAY TO A NEW LIFE

People were laying aside their old lives, packing up their things and driving into a new life in Westmoreland, beyond this sign. I was Sherlock. I had unlocked the mystery, I had communicated God's message through thought transference. A new world lay upon the horizon. Pessimism was replaced with optimism, and on this Sunday a dream had been presented to all men and women as they slept. They had awoken with great joy and a certainty that life would never be the same. It would be better. I stood, arms folded, beaming.

Jesus stirred and woke at that moment, making me jump.

'Areet, man!' he exclaimed in thick Geordie.

'Not bad, man, not bad,' I replied.

He rose in white boxers and headed into the corridor, and I heard the door of the toilet open and close. A Geordie Jesus? His face resembled the illustrations of Jesus I had seen. When he returned, he climbed back into bed, stretched and closed his eyes. When he next awoke the world would be complete. I turned suddenly as someone else entered the room. It was the pale man with slicked black hair. He approached me.

'Now, son, what're you up to?' He looked searchingly at the piece of paper I had been writing on.

'Writing.'

'Writing what, son?'

'About what I see.'

I was careful not to give much away that would betray my secret activities. For several minutes the man with the slicked black hair looked over the paper, concerned. Then his expression lightened and he handed it back to me.

'Right-o, son,' he said, and left the room.

'What are you in for, then?' Jesus asked, sitting up wearily.

'To help you and your father,' I replied shakily. He laughed crazily.

'That'd be right. Me fatha's a great man so he is. Eee, I'm

21

knacka'd.' He rubbed his eyes.

'You've had a tiring time,' I spoke soothingly.

'Aye, that I 'ave. Pass us that newspapa will ya, chief?'

I passed a paper across to Jesus which lay on the floor beside me. I was beginning to doubt his authenticity.

3

The large frame of Dr Rogers came lumbering into the room just as it began to get dark. I was still at the window. Jesus was sleeping once more, knees raised beneath the sheets in that peculiar manner of his. Dr Rogers seemed rather more sprightly than he had been previously.

'Right, James, I'd like you to follow me along the corridor. We're moving you into a room of your own, since one of the patients has moved out. Your mother's been. She gave me a bag with some of your stuff in it. And she left you some food and drink if you want it. It's all through here.'

I followed him further up the corridor to the final door on the right, which opened up into a room about 10 feet by 12 in size. My bag lay upon the bed, and I opened it eagerly to see what was inside. A pair of pyjamas, a Walkman with one of my tapes loaded in it, a 'Rumpole' book in the Penguin 60s miniature format, my glasses and my contact lens box. I had forgotten all about my contacts.

'Your mother asked me to get you to take those out before you do anything else,' said Dr Rogers, and I did as he asked. To my surprise, they came out quite easily. My eyes were not tired, and quite fresh.

'Now then, have yourself a rest. Your mother's coming in the morning to see how you're getting on. See if you can surprise her.'

'What do you mean, "surprise her"?' I asked.

'Well, you know, get some sleep.'

'But I'm not tired.'

'You should be, son, you've been up long enough. Anyway, I'll see you in the morning.'

He departed, closing the door behind him. It was 5.30 p.m.

now, and the sky had turned jet black. Cars made a swishing sound as they passed smoothly by the window. A large window beside my bed was covered by a white blind, and occasionally this was moved aside as someone looked in on me from the corridor, a beam of light shining momentarily on my face.

I eventually decided to take the sandwich my mother had set out for me, unwrapping the tin foil and devouring it quickly. The bacon made me thirsty. A small can of Diet Coke and a full bottle of milk lay on the bedside table. I opened the Diet Coke and drank some, as well as a gulp of milk. I was glad of the refreshment.

Placing the earphones in, I switched on my Walkman and stretched out on the bed, which was hard but comfortable. Songs from *The Love Album: Volumes I and II* filled my ears. I analysed their content. I was the subject of these songs. Each artist had recorded specifically for me. I was everything a girl could wish for. I would heal the pain of the broken-hearted. Melancholic tunes affected me deeply and I listened with seriousness to the cries for help, the despair of lost love and broken dreams. I looked out into the night sky and longed to help these women, to let them know that *I* cared, that *I* understood.

The road was now relatively quiet. Cars went by in twos now, as pairs of lovers followed each other through the night air and into their future. The animals went in two by two. As Eastwood became more sparse, the lonely hearts of the world chased each other into Westmoreland. The bright lights of the metropolis beckoned. Happiness and fulfilment was every man and woman's right. I observed its achievement through the window beside me, as cries of joy poured into my ears, partially drowning the music. A beam of light fell upon my face as someone from the corridor looked in. They could now sense my progress. *They* knew what was going on.

Vehicles took on a sleeker appearance in the night, the

streetlight licking their chassis as they passed by. They mostly appeared black. Each pair was segregated by a car with a sloped rear, which glowed yellow. These were agents, ensuring the safe passage of each pair into the new world.

The silhouette of an 'H' was projected upon the wall opposite me as I lay in the darkness of my room. Holmes. Sherlock Holmes. The connection was obvious. I had opened the gateway to a new life, I was the secret detective who had solved the mystery. Conan Doyle had envisaged just such a person over a hundred years ago, and here he now was. I had all the characteristics: boundless energy, a sharp intelligence and a great ability to apply logical skills. The letter 'H' also marked the moment in which the movement of humanity to Westmoreland had begun in earnest. Sherlock Homes were the key to the future.

I now knew that the light coming through the window, and the eye which looked searchingly into the room was the Ancient Mariner from Coleridge's poem. I had begun to look with an imaginative eye and saw God the Father in all the world around me, as the Mariner had warned the Wedding-Guest to do. He approved of my activities and was checking to see that I continued to gaze with imagination. I was awakening characters from textual entrapment. Doors were opening for the benefit of all.

The results of my work were continuing to surprise and enchant me. I had spun a complex web of reasoning in order to catch my dreams, and this web was continuing to expand beyond my control, as though it had a plan of its own. I would be taken along wherever the web should take me. I had no choice but to follow it.

I sat by the window, the lamplights beaming past, the liquid-looking metal following. A line of streetlights lay either side of the street. The dual carriageway was long gone. Streetlights networked their way across the hill, beyond which lay the homes of the future.

I heard a click as the door opened, and the man with slicked hair sat himself upon a chair in my doorway and began to read. I was fascinated to discover he was now dressed in a rather expensive dinner suit. He had previously been dressed in blue jeans, shirt and scruffy-looking brown pullover. Yet there he sat, oblivious to my fascination, engrossed in a large leather-bound book.

I decided to change into the pyjamas my mother had left, climbed under the covers and picked up the 'Rumpole' book. *Rumpole and the Younger Generation* was the title, and I could remember several times at home picking it up to read it, then tiring of it several pages in. I could not imagine why my mother had picked this book out for me. Nevertheless, I began it, after switching on the dim lamp above me by playing around with the switches beside my bed until I found the right one. 'I, Horace Rumpole, barrister at law, sixty-eight next birthday, Old Bailey hack ...' I stopped. I couldn't take it all in. There was simply too much information. I reread this first line or so. Again the same problem. I persevered to the end of the first page, which seemed to take an excruciating amount of time. I tried reading the next page, but gave up half-way down it. I did not feel in any way tired.

As I placed my own book on the bedside table and switched off the lamp, I saw that the man with slicked black hair's book had shrunk to about half its previous size. As I watched in astonishment, the book continued to shrink. Eventually it was around half the size of his hands. I closed my eyes for several moments to confirm that this was true. As I opened them again, the book was once more full size. It was my life story. The power that held my life together had become instilled in this book. The man would occasionally lean forward and scrutinise a certain page. The book continued to alter in size.

I desperately needed the toilet. I rose from the bed.

'Why don't you get yourself some sleep, fella?' the man asked.

'Need the toilet.' I felt like a little boy who has the indignity of having to explain his needs to an older person.

'Right-o.' He placed the book face down. I went to see what it was. 'Don't you touch that!' the man snapped. 'That's not for you to see. Now come on.'

I followed him down the corridor and to the right. I noticed a number of wooden doors with glass windows in them had been closed, splitting the corridor up into three or four sections. In each of the distant corridors someone was pacing up and down. It was representative of Jesus, biding his time through the ages before his return in the Golden Age.

I went into a cubicle, as the man waited immediately outside. Why was he so touchy about me seeing my own life story? It would surely help in my efforts to decipher further coding and messages. I washed my hands thoroughly as I looked at myself in the mirror. Obvious dark circles were now forming beneath my eyes, which seemed to protrude button-like above them.

'Aye, ya startin' ta look knackered, son,' the man with slicked black hair remarked. He was no longer wearing his expensive-looking dinner suit, and had changed once more into jeans, shirt and scruffy brown jumper. I had no idea how he had transformed so quickly, but then this was no ordinary hospital ward.

He escorted me back towards my room, and then asked if I'd prefer to watch a little TV before going to bed. I followed him to the desk on which the TV sat, exactly opposite my room. It was a rather fuzzy picture, but I could make out a snooker table and could see the match situation plainly enough, the colour and position of the balls.

'Now, son,' the man said, sitting back in a comfortable-looking leather chair, 'can you tell me what happens next?'

I considered carefully. 'He'll pot the red into the top right, then take on the blue, and miss.'

'OK.'

I watched in wonder as my prediction came true. The man

was not amazed in the least. He had evidently dealt with visionaries before.

'Now, do the same again.' He rolled himself a cigarette, and although I never smoked, the idea of one had never been so attractive as at that moment. It had been a long strange day.

'I think Williams will pot the red to the middle, the blue, the red to the bottom left, the black, then win the frame.'

After several minutes, we saw Mark Williams pot the balls the way as I had predicted and went on to win the frame. The man put a cupped left hand over his wet-looking head, and took a big drag on the cigarette he had made.

'You're very good,' he said.

As he slurped some coffee and began rolling another cigarette I noticed a packet of small Panama cigars, similar to the kind Rumpole was depicted smoking on the front cover of my book, and a red pack of Berkeley. I was tempted.

'You'd better get yourself back to bed. It'll be morning pretty soon.'

I did as he said, and he resumed his seat outside my door. I lay gazing at the letter 'H', then turned to watch the road once more, which was now still. The wind and the man turning the pages of his book were all I could hear. I turned evidence over in my head. Panama, Berkeley, Panama, Berkeley. I had written the Rumpole book under the pen name John Mortimer. I was Rumpole; and the Panama cigars were mine.

I lay silent for what seemed like hours, gazing at the ceiling, listening to the sound of wind. The man looked up from his book when he heard a door close somewhere behind him, then resumed his reading. I heard a woman's footsteps on the floor above me, heels clicking against the surface, then a sound of running and a car revving up in the car-park below. The land of Westmoreland beckoned. It remained for me to stay put until the entire hospital was empty and Eastwood was evacuated before I could follow this lady, the girl of my dreams. Rachel Lockwood.

An old lady approached, her hair a bushy grey perm. The man with slicked hair rose and disappeared down the corridor, taking his book with him. The old lady sat, her hands loosely clasped, her large spectacles and plump frame giving her the appearance of a wizened old owl. Soon she lit a cigarette and began reading a magazine. I shifted my gaze to the window, sometimes trying to close my eyes and sleep, but failing every time.

4

The sky became gradually lighter. I heard the first cries of seagulls and saw the first cars to use the road. My eyes felt weighted. The old lady rocked to and fro as she read. The air vent emitted warm air.

Soon it was light and the lady disappeared, closing my door behind her. I meditated upon the opposite wall. The 'H' had vanished with the darkness.

Some time later, my mother entered with my sister Victoria and Aunty Beryl. I said nothing. They had done nothing to prevent my imprisonment. I felt like a monkey that had been caged up for testing, yet my family had put up no fight to keep me.

'Morning, James!' my mother exclaimed, trying to sound cheerful. She was still pale, and I could see she was trying to be cheerful.

'Hi.'

'Did you get any sleep?'

'No.'

'Oh, why not?' Victoria asked angrily, sitting down in the corner in disgust. She passed her fingers through her dark hair.

'Just couldn't. Anyway, why should I?' I noticed my mother shoot an agonised look at my aunt.

'James, you need your sleep. You always have,' she said.

'What's in the bag?' I asked. My mother's expression changed suddenly.

'Oh, I've brought you a bacon sandwich, some orange juice and some cheese sandwiches for lunch.'

'Thanks.'

'You'd better have the bacon ones now before they go cold. Have you been washed?'

'No.'

My mother turned to my aunt and sister.

'That's disgraceful, isn't it? You'd think they could have made him have a wash.'

I unwrapped the sandwich.

'You know what this means, don't you? The bread represents God, and the bacon represents humanity. God's goodness protects humanity.'

'Listen, James, it's just a sandwich. I don't know where you got all this stuff from, but it's rubbish, do you hear? Beryl, what on earth's he on about? Eat it up, James!'

I did as I was told. My mother sat down in some agitation, then left the room suddenly.

'So what've you been doing, James? Have you read your book?' my Aunty Beryl asked, looking across at the Rumpole. She spoke calmly and gently, her blue eyes relaxed, in contrast to my mother's dark, anxious gaze.

'I couldn't. I kept forgetting what I'd just read. Anyway, I had other work to do. At night they put me through my Divine training. It's vital for the meeting of east and west and the development of Westmoreland.'

My aunt looked at me in bewilderment, then at my sister.

'What *are* you on about?' asked Victoria, half angry, half shocked. 'You're talking rubbish!'

'You just don't understand,' I said, my head rested on my pillow, facing away from them, sipping on my carton of orange juice. I could hear my mother's raised voice in the corridor.

She re-entered, looking flustered and began talking frustratedly, as though I wasn't in the room.

'Well, I said to the nurse, "You'd think you could give him some sleeping tablets while he was like this!" "Eee naw pet, we need a doctor's permission," she said. Where does she think we are? We're *in* a bloody hospital now!' She was livid.

'Barbara, calm down!' my Aunty pleaded,

31

'Yes, but Beryl they could've washed him, or told him to wash himself. I don't know. Come on son take off your 'jamas and we'll wash you.'

I stripped, humiliated to be washed by hand for the first time since I was five years old. My mother worked quickly with a hand towel, and then washed my hair in the sink of the ensuite, which I had never previously noticed was there. For all the humiliation and indignation it caused me, I did feel better when I had been dried off. This done, my mother and sister sat back, eyeing me with pity as they would an invalid or wounded animal.

'So, are you gonna do us a favour and get yourself better? We're worried sick here!' said my mother, laughing then removing a tear that trickled down her face.

'What do you mean?' I asked.

My question killed the conversation. A void lay between us. They just did not get it. I needed to get to that station. This was of global importance. The whole world, not just the north-east of England, must know. I felt betrayed by them. They were ridiculing me through their ignorance. God would be disappointed.

After a pause of around ten minutes they all got up.

'Right. We're going. Oh, James, give me that watch,' my mother said, taking it from my wrist. 'I'm frightened you'll damage it. Now please try and get some sleep. The doctors say you'll be fine in a few days if you sleep it off. Your father will be coming to see you on his way back from work. See if you can at least ease his mind. He's worried sick.'

'Sleep what off?' I asked. My sister rolled her eyes. My mother began to cry. They left the room, slumped-shouldered.

Initially taking heed of my mother's words, I lay for some time attempting to sleep. A pain was developing behind my eyes, and I determined to keep them closed for a couple of hours. But it was no good. My lids flickered open like elastic. I was too interested in the external world to worry about the internal needs of rest. I shifted over to the window and prepared for another vigil of conundrums and puzzles. The development of Westmoreland. I knew what I was doing. The work must go on regardless of the opinions of others.

I was woeful at the loss of my watch and wondered why I'd let my mother take it. I had absolutely no concept of time. I kept checking with a so-called nurse, and my own predictions for the time of day were always a long way from reality. My memory was shot. I would backtrack to thinking it was 7.00 a.m. by the light of the sky, before I thought long and hard and remembered the visits of some of my family. I became conscious of some trickery at work. I added it all up – nurses, doctors, hospital, no sleep, general concern. This, however, was something which also receded into the vagueness of dubious memory.

I saw people running on the hill with various brightly coloured vests on. Evidently a competition. Survival of the fittest. Darwin was right about that one at least. I could see part of their course now, through some boggy-looking wooded areas, over a stile, on to the open hillside, up the hill and out of sight. One of the runners looked remarkably like my Uncle John. I'd met him only once at the age of one, but remembered a photograph I had seen. Perhaps he was trying to assist in my problem-solving, or point out that he was to be a key player in the future of Westmoreland. Maybe *that* was what he was doing living in Denmark – spreading the word throughout Scandinavia. Maybe he had already seen the vision. Maybe *he* was the disciple named John.

The last of the runners soon disappeared. A child was moving along the flat base of the hill now, just in from the road. He was kicking a huge ball, which looked about three feet in circumference, then walking up to it and kicking it again, precisely the same distance every time. A woman who was evidently his mother walked behind with a black Labrador. Her jacket puffed out and the figures seemed to be blown along by a strong wind. I could hear it whirring away through the window. The clouds stood high in the blue sky as though they'd been blown away too.

I felt stupefied, gazing at everything with an involuntary intensity. There was nothing surprising, nothing new to behold and to sing inward or outward praises for. All I saw was traffic, now back to being modern in average age, and a hill in place of some housing estate. I had received no signs today, other than my mother's distress and a hint that somehow an uncle was involved.

And yet, as I watched, things began to happen again. The clouds were moving more quickly, forming letters that in turn formed the words:

YOU CAN NOW

I felt a little afraid, but I knew what it meant. It was up to me to create my own path to Westmoreland. I needed to escape. *Carpe diem.* I saw the car-park below me, and spotted one of the cars had a numberplate ending in YCN. It was a black Porsche. Evidently this was to be my transport. The key would be hidden somewhere, and if I found it, I could be away. Yet maybe this was another test. I kept watching, waiting for the truth to surface.

As time drifted by, I lost touch with my concepts. The theories I had built for myself and the ideas I was working with were snagging on the fact that the visions were no longer coming thick and fast. Now I had begun to slightly doubt the general authenticity of my theories. I knew how long it was since I'd slept. I knew that something was wrong. Yet drunken-mindedness prevented my complete escape from the surreal. Looking at the hill still afforded me great pleasure. It had not been there when I first arrived, and was evidence that I was witnessing something extraordinary. Yet it terrified me to think that I had no tangible evidence that I was right about anything. What if I was wrong and the world was going to Hell? I was unable to follow these thoughts through, to create a chain of reasoning, and therefore such ideas continued to be transitory. After each momentary lapse into doubtfulness I went back to where I started, searching for clues.

The sky clouded over in thick dark grey, and very soon rain was belting across the glass. I went to the toilet, then climbed into bed, my limbs weary and my head aching. I took off my glasses and shut my eyes.

After a while I heard the handle of my door turn, and the door click shut. I opened my eyes, having still failed to sleep and reached for my glasses. A middle-aged man with greying hair, suit and tie and dark blue overcoat was seated in a chair at the foot of my bed. His blue eyes looked out at me seriously, almost angrily. Was it God? Was he annoyed at my recent doubt? I decided to ask him.

'Are you God?'

The figure seemed disturbed by this question, fidgeted, but gave no reply. He continued his blank, serious gaze. And then he rose, closing the door gently behind him as he left.

I rolled over and attempted to recover the ground I'd lost on route to sleepiness, but it was no good. My eyes were curious, my brain still buzzed. The day passed away without any further activity, as though the world was in total stasis. As night fell, the horizon turned a delicate pink, and for some time I sat enraptured by its beauty. I was still cared for after all.

The pinks dripped over the dark-blue skyline like watercolour paints, and a few stars began to sparkle out of the darkness. I let the darkness fill the room, feeling no need of the lamp. Shortly after, the man with slick hair entered and asked me to follow him.

He sat back in the black leather chair.

'Have a look at these magazines,' he said plainly. I did. They were filled with extraordinarily high-quality images, and articles concerning the future of the planet. Most of these articles seemed familiar, their content connected with the ideas I had been generating over the past few days and nights. I noticed that they were all Sunday supplements. They reaffirmed that the great Change had begun to take place on Saturday night. At intervals I would find an article that fitted in with the Westmoreland idea, and exclaim aloud: 'Oh, right!' It all served to reignite my zest for the importance of the Golden Age.

'That was why the classic cars stopped going past the window,' I said, 'because I'd stopped believing!'

'Ah, yes.' The man seemed to understand. He considered, carefully rolling another cigarette.

'And where were these cars going?' he asked.

'Oh, to Westmoreland, the land of the future. You see God wants humanity to move on, to improve and move into the Golden Age. Eastwood is to be left behind by March the third. That's when I'll be meeting up with the representatives of both worlds, Eastwood and Westmoreland.'

'I see. That'll do for now,' the man said, flicking some ash into his tray, 'go and rest, and we'll speak some more later.'

I went back to my room and got into bed. The man was eyeing me through the glass window, now stripped of its blind. The wind rumbled on into the night as I gazed out into the darkness.

5

A loneliness began to creep up on me, and the divide between myself and the outside world was more obvious than ever before. The old lady from the previous night and a young man in his twenties sat at the threshold of my room, but they seemed distant and uncaring. The isolation became oppressive. I was being observed, like a rare species. The two talked excitedly amongst themselves for some time, in whispers.

As I watched them, their importance grew. The old lady took on the role of Mother Nature. She cared for the overall outcome of the world, safeguarded its progress. The young man, in his green sweatshirt and short black hair represented the youth of the modern age and the Golden Age to come. He was part of the transition. They laughed contentedly, as though they expected great things to come.

Hours seemed to pass as I watched them. I moved to the chair by the window, inhibited by their presence. Eventually I heard them rise. I turned to see the old lady pick her cigarettes and lighter off the floor, then she and the young man headed off down the corridor.

The ward seemingly empty, I hurried to get my clothes on, wanting to escape this claustrophobia, this prison. I did not care where I went. I packed my bag, but was daunted to hear footsteps outside my door and see a stocky man of medium height and spiky dark hair in a black shirt and trousers uttering the surprising words: 'Right, son, let's go. We'll have to hurry or we'll be late.'

I finished packing and went silently along with him. I was grateful of the transport. He'll drop me at the station and I can be on my way, I thought. It'll be nice to get away.

We reached the end of the corridor and the man pressed the

button for the elevator.

'I'm Dave,' he said, impatiently tapping the carpet with his left foot, 'hope you've enjoyed yourself 'ere.'

'It's been alright. Very strange.'

'Aye. Tha's some daft characters in 'ere, like,' he agreed, 'you've gotta watch yourself'.'

The elevator arrived and I realised this man understood me. He had come to assist in my escape. I looked at him, an earring in his left ear, alert blue eyes, chewing gum. Maybe he was part of the Westmoreland clan.

'You from Westmoreland?' I asked.

'Nor, man, Easterside. Middlesbrough. You from Hartle-pool, aye?' I nodded. So that was it. He was one of the people readying to help east meet west. He was from the east side, heading for the west side.

We stepped out of the elevator and headed for a large white vehicle in the car-park, which I realised was an ambulance as we approached it. I was told to get in the back, and the man started the engine and steered the ambulance round the front of the hospital, to Accident and Emergency. He got out and helped a couple of old women into the vehicle, then set off. We then headed out of Hartlepool and on to the A19.

* * *

The motion of the ambulance sparked a remembrance. I found myself in my parents' car, my mother driving, my father in the passenger seat, my sister and I in the back. I looked out on to Elwick Village green. Some kids were playing football. I recognised John Southport strolling to his favourite of the two pubs, The McOrville. I saw him spot our car and wave to my father, who waved back as my mother pulled over to let him out.

'Right, have a good time, James. I'll say hi to the lads for you.'

'Thanks. See you later on.' On Saturdays I usually went to

The McOrville with my father to play darts with John South-port and a young Dutchman who worked behind the bar, Ruud Van Arnhem. Ruud used to take all the money out of the fruit machine so that no one else, including myself, could win.

I moved into the vacant passenger seat and my mother drove on. As we passed down the narrow, winding bank that led out of Elwick, my mother began her usual monologue about not drinking too much, that I was underage anyway, that smoking was to be avoided at all costs.

'Because once you have one, you'll just want more, and you won't be able to afford them.'

I watched the silhouettes of trees waving in the countryside beyond the A19, and wondered what was going on in the distant farmhouses. The men would be in the pub, the women would be watching TV awaiting their drunken return. Rachel lived on a farm in Richmond. I checked my watch. In 20 minutes I would be with her.

The car turned into the dark winding road that led to Hardwick Hall. I looked out at the skeletal oaks and bushy conifers which lined the entrance. The large main building came into view, a ghostly white through the darkness. Tremors went through my stomach as I began to simmer with excite-ment. I liked parties. Rachel had sent me an enticing letter only a week before. *I'll be wearing a red velvet dress.*

We moved around to the back of the main building, and my mother pulled up beside the door of the country club. I could hear music thumping. I was late.

'Well, take care. And have a good time,' she said.

'I will,' I replied, as she kissed me on the cheek.

'Yes, have a good time.' My sister looked jealous, arms folded. I stepped out of the car, taking my entrance ticket from my pocket.

* * *

The ambulance driver shouted something and I realised we were at the Billingham turn off. I tried to remember more of the night I had flashed back to, but it was useless. I could not remember any more of the party, nor when it happened. I wanted to catch its significance.

We dropped off the two old women at the same housing estate in Billingham, their houses two or three blocks apart. Nobody said a word except the driver, who shouted the women's names as we arrived at their houses.

The road came to a roundabout and we drifted steadily towards Middlesbrough, but Dave was in no hurry. The sky was becoming a little lighter but was still practically black. I guessed it was around seven as the roads were almost empty. Again, I was conscious of a growing fear. We had missed the turn off for the railway station. And why was I being transported by ambulance? Did the man mean to hurt me? Had I done something?

'Where are you taking me?' I asked.

'St Luke's Hospital,' he said, yawning. Another hospital. Why all these hospitals?

The ambulance chugged its way down a long, straight road, then turned into a driveway which led to a group of old buildings. The sign on the gate read: 'South Tees Medical Trust'.

We passed a number of medical buildings, all of worn redbrick, and came to a larger redbrick building. 'The Roseberry Centre for Young People' the sign explained. A stern-looking woman of around 50 stood in the doorway. She had short grey hair, and was noticeably tall. She greeted me in a foreign accent as I came out of the back door of the ambulance.

'You maast be James! I'm Vilma! Ve hope you vill like it here. I vill do all in my power to make you feel at home! Follow me.' I immediately took a dislike to her. In spite of her attempts at cheeriness, I detested the regimental cant of her speech. The staccato rhythm in it chilled me deep inside.

Wilma was tall, her face quite aged with deep circles beneath the eyes, and sterile pale blue irises.

She took me into a living-room, long yet stuffy. Evidently the windows had not been opened for some time. The walls were yellow and there were pool and table tennis tables. Magazines were scattered on couches at the far end of the room. A large tank containing brightly coloured fish was against the farthest wall. In a corner by the couches was an old TV. A patio door opposite the entrance to the room looked out into the vast hospital complex, which looked grim and imprisoning in the early morning light.

'Everyone's still in bed. You get vake-up call every day at eight.'

She took me through to another room, which was beside the main door. It was large and spacious, with a desk that faced away from a large window, filing cabinets, medical books, and a small window at the far end, which looked into a much smaller room. Through the window I admired the extensive green lawn and rows of conifers, which spread up to the gate.

'This is the office. You're not allowed in here unless ve say so.' She had now dropped her light breezy tone and become suddenly serious.

Across from the office was a waiting-room with magazines and comics laid out in scattered piles. The walls were a bright blue colour.

'Now, I'll show you the kitchen.'

Wilma took me down a long, dirty-looking corridor to the kitchen. The yellow paintwork was unseen to, the brown carpet worn and decrepit. There was dust everywhere which irritated my eyes. We entered a grubby-looking old kitchen to the left which none the less looked well-supplied. Wilma then took my arm and showed me the dining-room on the opposite side of the corridor, opened a cupboard and showed me where all the cutlery and table-cloths were stowed away after each meal. There were board games in there too, chess, snakes and

41

ladders, cards and so on.

'If you could start and set the tables now, I'll go and get the others up. After breakfast ve'll show you your room and you can haf a rest.'

Disgruntled at being ordered around by a stranger, I nevertheless got on with the job. After all, I was hungry, and perhaps compliance was the only way I was going to get food. That staccato woman surely had a bite.

It occurred to me that I had no idea what I was doing there. Maybe I was to give a helping hand to the ward, to try to help people in some way. And yet this was not in Wilma's tone. There was a masterly tone she used with me, that staccato ...

I sat and waited, the tables all set. Wilma came back, thanked me and showed me to the toilet. The toilet was cold, its frosted glass windows merging colours into interesting forms. I washed my hands, counting to 20 with cold water and 20 with hot, using plenty of soap. I had to keep some semblance of method, of order. I walked down the corridor and met a roomful of children in the dining-room. They stared, then continued their quiet, controlled conversations. Wilma entered suddenly.

'You sit here, James.' She pointed to an empty table set for three. 'Katie'll be down in a minute. She's more your age.' The children laughed in exasperation, 'NOW STOP THAT, KIDS!' she screamed. She meant it, and the kids knew. Wilma smiled at me, snapping suddenly into a more benign mood. The kids were silent again, eating their Cornflakes and Weetabix.

Wilma placed some toast in front of me, and I buttered a piece and began to eat. A tall girl with short, neatly bobbed blonde hair sat down beside me. She had sparkling blue eyes, but the dark circles beneath them resembled my own. Opening a box of Cornflakes, she turned her lively eyes towards me and smiled.

'Hiya there! You're new here, aren't you?'

'Yeah, just arrived. What's your name?'

42

'Katie Waters. And yours?'

'James Richard Thomas Fountain Berkeley.'

Katie burst into laughter. 'Bloody Hell, that's some name, isn't it!'

'It's my new name. My name in Westmoreland.'

'Westmoreland? That's where you're from is it?'

'No. I'm from Eastwood, but Westmoreland is where I'm headed, as a man of the future. Humankind is resolving itself. The world is moving into Westmoreland collectively, as the bad filters out of the world. Then Christ will return.'

Katie had put down her spoon and was staring at me, her forehead corrugated, her blue eyes wary, maybe even afraid. By now, some of the other kids were also looking up from their food. Their misapprehension was frustrating, made me afraid too. Suddenly, she picked up her spoon again and recommenced eating.

'Well, I'm a student at Middlesbrough Art College. I'm in my second year. You'll be still at school are you?'

'Yes. I'm sixteen. I'm doing my GCSEs this year. How old are you?'

Katie's expression brightened. 'You don't ask a girl that!' she laughed, 'but at least now you're making some sense. I'm nineteen.' She paused, then laughed again. I liked her laugh. 'You're a funny lad. I've been needing someone to make me laugh in this place. Things can get so boring.'

We finished breakfast, then I helped Katie clear the tables. We took the plates and bowls through to the kitchen, and as Katie washed them, I dried. Wilma seemed always to be somewhere in the background, watching.

'D'ya like Oasis, James?'

'They're alright. I bought *Morning Glory*.'

Katie smiled, and then sang:

'*So Sally can wait, she knows it's too late*
As we're walkin' on by,

Her soul slides away, but don't look back in anger
I heard you say.'

'I heard *you* say, Katie.'

'I heard *you* say, James!' We laughed together. She had a kind smile.

When the pots were washed and dried and put away we headed down to the living-room and sat on opposite couches. Katie eyed me curiously.

'You should meet some of the others.' Two girls who looked slightly younger than me were approaching, having just finished a game of pool. 'You two, this is James. James, this is Judith, and this is Helen.'

'Hi, James,' they said in unison.

'Pleased to meet you both.' They sat either side of me. Judith sat to my left. She wore black jeans and a purple woolly jumper. Her face was pale against her long black hair. She wore gothic-style eyeshadow and eyeliner which made her beautiful green eyes gleam like emeralds through the darkness. Helen was more sedately dressed, in blue jeans and a baggy white *Simpsons* T-shirt with Homer drinking a can of Duff beer. She had very light blonde hair and sad brown eyes.

'Where do you come from, then?' Judith asked.

'Hartlepool. They transferred me by ambulance today.'

Katie looked at me suddenly. 'Eh? I thought you were from "Westmoreland" or whatever it was?'

'I am – at the moment. But – I'm not sure it's all been sorted yet. You see we can't be sure it's all gone to plan until I meet these two guys on the third of March. Then I'll know where we stand.'

'You a drug dealer or something, then? I mean you're talking about contacts and meeting up with guys and sorting stuff out, aren't you?' Judith asked.

'That's what I was thinkin'. Or a druggy, more like. He acts like he's on LSD,' said Katie.

44

'What? No, I don't think you understand. The people at the Hartlepool General did, and helped and encouraged me with my work.'

'Work? This is a *hospital*, you weirdo! You're not a doctor or a nurse!'

'Katie, this is my Divine training. God has singled me out as a visionary. This is what I do, and I don't have a choice.' I sat back in zen calm. I put my arms around the two girls beside me protectively. I felt responsible for them all, was grateful for their company. Helen sat in disinterested silence, looking at the floor. Katie's eyes gazed confusedly into Judith's, then flickered briefly into my own, before settling upon the fish tank. She didn't believe me, but I didn't blame her. People did not always believe visionaries, after all. But I liked her, and did not want to lose the friendship we had begun to build. Judith and Helen fidgeted uncomfortably beneath my arms. I leapt up off the couch.

'Katie, do you fancy a game of pool?' Her eyes brightened as she came back from the gloomy world at the bottom of the fish tank.

'Aye, alright!'

We walked over to the table and I selected a cue from the rack in the corner. They were interesting cues, constructed in three sections with patterned red metal at their joinings. I unscrewed them, then put them back together. Evidently they were special cues, enabling the player to play above his or her normal standard. Katie arranged the balls in the triangle.

'Right, James, you can break.'

'OK.'

I struck the white hard into the pack, and several of the balls flew on to the floor.

'Take it easy, James, or the nurses will stop you from playing!' Katie exclaimed.

'It's this cue, it's giving me special powers. I'll take one of the sections off.' I removed the small, lowermost section from my cue. Having replaced the fallen balls randomly on the table, Katie took her shot and potted a red cleanly into a corner pocket.

'The red balls represent love and the yellow balls represent harmony. The black ball represents hate, so we must be careful not to pot that ball until the end.'

'Look, James, I won't play you if you're gonna talk to me about this shit all the time. They're just coloured balls. Take your shot.'

Maybe she was right this time. I could not be right about everything. Maybe some things did have no meaning. But it would be impossible to describe my sense of distress when the black ball went in as I made a careless shot. To repair the damage, I took my cue and ran around the table tennis table 12 times, taking care to scrape the cue continuously against all of its sides. I was recalling the 12 disciples, warning them of the dangers that would come through my accidental sinking of the black ball, the help that would be required of them.

When I had completed this, I realised Katie was outside the patio door, facing away from me, smoking a cigarette. I went over to the door, which would not open.

'You're not vell enough to go out yet, James,' Wilma piped up. She had been watching me again. I did not trust her. 'I saw you, running around the table. Unless you stop doing zat, you vill never go out alone again.'

'You won't stop me forever. Soon you will understand.'

'Well, that's not my job. Dr Anderson vill be seeing you in a couple of hours' time. See if you can behave yourself between now and zen.'

6

The younger children I had seen at breakfast seemed to have disappeared, and Helen and Judith had been allowed out to a nearby cafeteria for lunch, so Katie and I were left alone. I sat absentmindedly on a couch, watching large yellow fish chasing tiny red and blue ones out of their territories in the tank. Katie had her art equipment laid out on the table between us, and sat opposite me working on strange and intricate designs. She used a fine black pen, and when she had finished she began filling gaps using brightly coloured felt pens. Her blue eyes were rapt in fierce concentration, contrasting with the ever-shifting gaze she possessed while not at work. Her right hand moved in skilful, assured arcs across the white paper.

'What are you working on?' I asked.

'Oh, just a project for college. It's a design for Bjork's new single, "Hyperballad".'

'It looks great – very complicated, though.'

'Thanks. But yeah, that's the point – Bjork's a complicated artist isn't she?'

Amongst a network of colours and swirls and arcs, she began to trace an outline of Bjork's face. Katie was the world's next great artist, I decided. The Roseberry Centre was a collection of bright young individuals, whose talents were being nurtured and developed.

A tall woman with closely cropped dark hair put her head around the door.

'James Fountain?' I looked up, surprised.

'Yes?'

'Just come this way, please.'

I said goodbye to Katie and followed the tall woman into the office. She looked about 30, and wore a dark-blue suit with gold buttons. The scent of Calvin Klein's *Obsession* breezed towards me. She sat behind the desk and took out a pair of modern, thick-rimmed spectacles.

'So, I'm Dr Anderson. I understand you've just come from Hartlepool General, am I right?' She was well-spoken, with a smooth, crisp voice. She arranged her spectacles with her left hand, turning a silver ball-point in the fingers of her right.

'Yes, they brought me here this morning in an ambulance. I went to a party on the way, to celebrate the beginning of the movement into Westmoreland.'

'A party? Oh, I don't think so. But then perhaps you are referring to the party your mother mentioned to me over the phone, that you attended on Saturday. Maybe you've suffered a flashback.'

'Flashback?'

'Yes,' she screwed up her eyes slightly and sat back in her chair, turning the pen slowly in her fingers. 'You see, I've had the head nurse here, Wilma, observe you over the past few hours. She's very experienced, and the symptoms she has noted down indicate drug abuse – specifically abuse of hallucinogens. Have you been using LSD?' She leaned forward.

'No. I've never used it. But I know people who have.'

'That's not the question I asked. Because if you have been there's no problem, as we have a counselling service that can help you out, and we can discharge you once the symptoms wear off. But in some cases this can take weeks.'

'No, I've never taken any drugs in my life.'

She looked me carefully in the eye.

'Your pupils are dilated and you have been displaying the exact symptoms of LSD or acid abuse. You have been, and are still, on a trip.'

'Well I know I'm on a trip. We all are. We're all moving from Eastwood into Westmoreland. God sent me a vision, and I need to meet two representatives on the third of March to ensure the deal goes through.' I gazed through the windows at the lawn, white, indifferent skies accentuating the green.

'What deal?'

'The resolving of the world. Life will never be the same.' I drew a question mark in the air and circled it ⊘. Dr Anderson stood up.

'Right. We'll take a urine sample from you, since I'm not sure when the blood sample they took at Hartlepool General will get back. And we'll do an E. E. G. scan tomorrow to check if the problem is epilepsy. But I don't think it is.'

'Epilepsy? You think I might have epilepsy? You don't understand – I'm a visionary. I am a messenger of God, a translator. I solve riddles and puzzles that no one else can solve!' I realised I was shouting. By now Dr Anderson was opening the door. Her mouth twisted at the edges.

'Let's go.' She seemed cool and indifferent, like the pale February sky. She led me back into the lounge, where Katie was still drawing, and left me. I heard the office door close shut. Katie looked up from her drawing.

'Do you want some lunch, James?' she asked.

'OK, I'm not really hungry though,'

'Oh, come on! You've got to eat. And there's plenty of stuff to make sandwiches with 'ere.'

I followed her through to the kitchen. Wilma was there making the evening meal. Katie opened the old fridge, and together we rummaged around.

'Do you like peanut butter, James?'

'No, not at all. Peanuts, yes, but not peanut *butter*.'

'I know. Disgusting isn't it? Anyway, we'll have to make do with boring cheese and ham.'

'That's great – they're my favourite anyway.'

Katie smiled. 'Easily pleased, eh? And we'd better make some for Annette. She's very sick, you know, so you won't have met her yet, stays in bed most of the day because she's so weak. She'll be down for her dinner later – never eats it, but always eats the sandwiches I make her. She's anorexic.'

49

We each made our own sandwiches, Katie wrapping Annette's up in cling film and placing them on the side. Annette would collect them later. We then moved to the dining-room. 'Wilma goes mad if we eat them in the lounge,' Katie said. I was glad someone agreed with me about Wilma.

'Oh, she's a cow. Just ignore her, I always do,' she said.

Wilma approached just as I was about to take a bite of the sandwiches.

'If you'll just take these pills, James. Dr Anderson asked me to give zem to you.' I considered. Dr Anderson had seemed kind, if a little cold. I was sure she didn't want to hurt me. So I took them from Wilma's hand and drank them down with the glass of water offered.

'Good boy.'

'I'm not taking them for you. I'm taking them for Dr Anderson.'

The afternoon passed away quickly as I talked with Katie. Remembering the loneliness of the previous day, I was thankful for the company. For most of the afternoon I was conscious of a great calmness. I liked to watch Katie drawing, her pretty eyes glancing up in surprise whenever she noticed my fascination.

I picked up a newspaper and attempted to read, but the letters seemed to merge into one. All I could read were headlines, though none of these seemed to reflect the news that *should* be reported. There was just the usual mixture of politics, murder, war, rape and financial complaint. Nothing about the great Change. Nothing of the wonder and mystery of life.

The fish tank intrigued me. Along its base were stones, tinged green with dirt. The water was clean enough to discern a dark lizard-like creature which crawled across the stones. Its yellow and black eyes stared back at me, before it curled itself up beneath one of the bridges.

I tried to work out whether the fish knew it was there, then realised they would forget about it every three minutes along

50

with everything else they had learned, according to current biological knowledge. How odd to have so short a memory span. I equated the lizard-like creature with the Devil, and the fish with humanity. Man forgot the Devil's presence with as great a regularity as the fish. Only when he moved around was man reminded of that presence. I watched one of the yellow fish as it investigated the lizard's bridge, its little black eyes seeming to discover it for the first time, then shooting away in fright as the creature moved one of its legs.

'The Devil's a crafty bugger isn't he? He waits until man has forgotten him, then does something to remind him he's still there.'

'What are you on about, James?' Katie asked, felt tip in hand. 'Talking like that all the time you'll never get home. You seemed fine earlier.'

'What do you mean? I'm only describing what's in the fish tank, what it represents.'

'Well, you can describe it to Wilma, I'm sure she'd love to hear it. I have to try and behave myself too, ya know. Especially now I'm nearly better.' I didn't understand the context in which she used the words 'fine' and 'better'. But I didn't want to irritate her. I watched as she began to use a blue crayon to draw a house over the text of a children's book she had picked off the shelf by the pool table.

Judith and Helen returned and began to watch afternoon TV. I was much moved by *Byker Grove* when a boy was dumped by his girlfriend for someone else. I recounted my own failings in love to Judith and Helen.

'Look, shut up, we're tryin' to watch this!' Judith snapped. I was disappointed. I thought she liked me. I got up and ran around the table tennis table 12 times, then found a beach ball beneath the pool table and began to kick it around the room with abandon. The three girls laughed at me.

'What yer doin', man? You're a blumin' looney!' This was an unknown voice, booming from the doorway behind me. I turned to see a large potbellied man with a red face and messy brown hair smiling back at me. 'I'm Tim. Tha've asked me to come in specially to look afta ya.' I disliked him instantly.

Soon, the younger children returned. They came noisily into the lounge, some shouting and giggling amongst themselves, others solitary and silent. I played a game of pool with a short, stocky boy called Robert. I beat him easily, and Robert stood staring in awe. I explained to him that it was partially to do with skill, but mostly to do with the power possessed by the cue. He ran off to tell his friends about it.

At dinner, Katie sat opposite me making fun of Tim. More tablets arrived. I agreed to take them, but only after a little encouragement from Katie. She said the only way to get out of the hospital was to comply with the doctor's wishes. Tim was sweating and red-faced as he ate his chilli, which had been prepared with too much powder by Wilma. I ate little, and instead watched a girl sitting alone by the doorway to my right. She had wavy brown hair down to her shoulders, and was eating with painful slowness. Each spoonful of chilli came steadily up to her mouth, and she would then pause and fixate upon the table with vexed brown eyes.

'Oh, that's Catherine,' Katie said, 'nobody knows what's wrong with her, she won't tell anyone.'

'She's obviously very upset,' I remarked. Tim put down his fork.

'Look, Mr Sensitive Posh Man. Eat yer dinner, and then yer can talk. Alright?'

'That's a bit harsh isn't it? Katie was talking to you just a minute ago!'

'Look, forget that. You haven't eaten yer dinner. Get on with it, or you'll be 'ere all night.'

'Yeah, man, you've gotta eat,' Katie chimed in.

'I hate people telling me what to do. I don't like this food. And I don't like you,' I said, pushing my plate away in defiance. Now Tim's face became redder still and he struck the table with his fist. A couple of the kids sniggered quietly. Judith looked across with the same look she had given me when I had been talking during *Byker Grove*. The emeralds flashed, they told me I was being foolish. I felt fired, a naughty twelve-year-old playing to the crowd, annoying the grown up, scoring secret brownie points.

'You'll regret talkin' ter me like that! You'll finish the lot before yer leave this room!' His big voice boomed. 'I never liked you posh buggers. Yer always want yer own way.'

After I'd eaten my ice cream as slowly as I could to annoy Tim, I helped Katie wash the dishes. He stood behind us, his loud breathing irritating me, each of his breaths expelling the smell of stale beer.

'Can't you just go away? We're trying to wash up here!' I exclaimed angrily. Evidently he was playing games, trying to wear me down like all the bullies I'd known at school.

'You – are – on – constant – observation. *Comprende*? But I'll stand in the corridor until your majesty has finished his washing up.'

I said nothing, glad that he'd gone from the room. Now we were free to talk as we wished.

'. . . but don't look back in anger, I heard *you* say, Katie!' I joked.

'I heard *you* say, James!'

I was glad that we were laughing again. Katie's voice dropped to a whisper.

'Seriously though, don't worry about Tim. Just go along with what he says. I don't like him either, he gives me the creeps. But if I pretend to like him he doesn't bother me.'

'Probably a bit too late for me, then.'

'Oh, he'll forget about it.'

Later in the lounge, everyone was gathered around the television except for a couple of the kids playing table tennis. As usual, *Coronation Street* and *Eastenders* were on in succession. I watched the male characters of Corra sinking frothy pints of real ale, the women scowling and complaining about money problems and bad sex. Outside the pub, their teenage kids bickered over girlfriends and boyfriends, talked about skipping school. School. It seemed a long time since I'd been there, and I felt I should be there. I was confused as to why I had been taken out of school, out of life, out of time.

Eastenders passed away without any incident that I could afterwards remember, my mind on other things. I thought about the connections I had made, about the 'flashbacks' that Dr Anderson had mentioned. But I was unable to follow these thoughts through to a conclusion, as they came to me from all angles and were too elaborate to analyse. As I shut my eyes I heard the voice of my mother, her tearful, panic-stricken face telling me to stop what I was doing. And then the hill, the moving fuzz replacing houses with hills and trees, progressing onwards. I alone knew what was really going on. I just needed time to think these ideas through.

Soon after the nine o'clock news we were all told it was time for bed, and escorted up the varnished wooden stairs. Tim seemed to have disappeared now, and a lean, shortish man in his fifties with closely shaved, balding grey hair and a bushy handlebar moustache punched in the security code which gave access to the upper level. The corridor had some ten doorways on either side of it. I was led to the room to the right of the secure door, and Katie waved me goodnight and entered a room two doors further up. Directly opposite my room was an office.

My room was small, with a single bed against the left wall as I walked in, a bedside table, a wardrobe and a large window directly opposite the door. The man with the bald head closed my curtains, then turned to leave the room.

'Now get your clothes off and get into bed. A fella's gonna come and watch your door. I'm Terry, by the way.'

I opened the wardrobe and found it full of clothes, some of which I recognised. Beneath the bed was a suitcase belonging to my parents. From the window I could see the great, sprawling car-park of St Luke's, nurses visible through the windows of the wards beyond, moving to and fro along dimly lit corridors. Streetlights gave off an orange glow, projecting the silhouette of an enormous oak tree against my closed door as I turned off the light.

I couldn't sleep. I rose and asked the man sitting outside my open door if I could go to the toilet. He had black hair and blunt eyes, which did not glint in the half-light. He sighed and put down his Wilbur Smith, folding the corner of the page he was up to. He would not let me close the bathroom door, and watched every movement I made with his lifeless eyes.

I returned to bed, my body weary, my mind alert. A branch tapped at the window as wind whirred on. I needed to get going. The tapping was a natural reminder from God that I had a mission to fulfil. I had already realised this was not the place I was intended to receive my Divine training, particularly after meeting Tim. I was wasting time. I searched my mind for a code, as the man at my door would no doubt require one in order that I might pass. Getting out of bed suddenly, I approached the doorway.

'James Richard Thomas Fountain Berkeley,' I said, in my crispest imitation of R. P. English.

'What?' the man asked in exasperation. I repeated myself. 'Look, get back into bed. It's late.' His voice was flat and lifeless as his eyes. He was almost certainly an agent guarding the next stage. I was certain this must be delivered in R. P.

'Panama, Berkeley, Panama.'

The man looked up from his novel.

'There's people tryin' to sleep here. Get yourself off to bed.' Again he was straightforward, showing no irritation. He was indicating I had given the wrong password. I reversed it.

'Berkeley, Panama, Berkeley.'

The man got out of his chair. 'Now, I won't tell you again. Get into bed.' I considered, my bare feet scraping the carpet, feeling a draft of air on my naked back. I had it.

'Sherlock Holmes. James Richard Thomas Fountain Berkeley. Sherlock Holmes.' The man jumped up once more, throwing down his book.

'Right, Mr Berkeley, get – yourself – to bed. I won't tell you again!' This time I did as he asked. I got into bed and stared at the ceiling.

Some time later, the man got up from his chair. As I heard him enter the bathroom, I reached for my clothes and put them on beneath the bed sheets. On his return, I prepared to try the password I had used originally. Maybe it would only work when I was fully clothed. I put on my shoes and approached the threshold.

'James Ri – ' I began.

'What are you doing dressed? Take your clothes off, son, and get into bed. Ya daft as a brush, man!'

So I was wrong this time. This was not the right moment to use the password. I decided that there would be another night when a representative of Eastwood would pick me up and take me to the next stage of my quest, like the ambulance driver who had collected me at Hartlepool General. I lay still, trying to be patient. It was all a matter of time.

Suddenly, the man re-entered and flicked on the light. He was carrying a glass of water and a tablet.

'Now, take this son, and you'll be able to get back to sleep.'

'I haven't been to sleep yet. Not for four nights.'

'Four nights? Well hopefully this'll work. Ya need ya sleep.' He was right, four nights was too long. I took the tablet, then got back into bed and closed my eyes. The light went out. But still my mind shone bright, and thoughts of Eastwood and Westmoreland sped through my mind, as I lay imagining what the Golden Age now looked like as it approached completion. I saw myself, the champion of the new age, being welcomed back into society, a riot of cheers and laughter and celebration filling my ears.

7

Gradually, the room grew lighter, and I opened the curtains. White clouds stood high in the blue sky like ships in a never-ending sea. Though the sudden brightness pained my eyes somewhat, I was alert and interested in the skyline before me. The pain receded so that I no longer needed to squint, and I put on my glasses.

The vast hospital complex lay below me, both opposite and to the left, forming a bottomless rectangle. The car-park was almost empty in the early morning. Directly opposite was an enormous boiler with steam constantly pouring out through the chimney. Away to the right were the North Yorkshire Moors, a welcome burst of green amongst the dull modern red brick of the hospital. Further to my right lay a distant motorway, cars the size of ants beginning to crawl across it.

I saw the connection immediately. Industry was represented by the boiler opposite. Imagination was represented by the North Yorkshire Moors. And commerce was represented by the motorway, which led to the city of Newcastle. So nothing had changed. The same designs I had envisaged in Hartlepool were applicable here in Middlesbrough. I was being shown the vision from different locations, that it was applicable to the whole world. I was being reminded of the three key elements that were to make up the formation of Westmoreland. Civilisation required industry, imagination and commerce in order to succeed. I allowed these thoughts to settle themselves in my mind.

When I turned round I saw that the man had taken his chair and Wilbur Smith book and gone, leaving me in solitude. I looked into the corridor. Outside the room next to me, two young men sat at an open doorway, discussing something and laughing in low whispers. The one nearest my door turned round, his spiky dark hair glistening with gel. He was about 23.

'Go back to bed. It's only six-forty-five,' he whispered. 'I'll tell you when it's time to get washed.' He was very polite. But I was itching to get moving, and went reluctantly back to my bed.

Hours seemed to pass as I lay with my eyes magnetically clamped on the door, awaiting the call. I focussed on my goal, to wait until the man from Westmoreland came to transport me to the final stage of my training.

Eventually the young man came to my door. He introduced himself as Charlie. His virtually flawless young skin and cheerful voice were a striking contrast to the ruggedness of the Wilbur Smith reader. Maybe the older man had got younger. They had the same eyes, after all.

The young man insisted that I have a bath before dressing. I told him I had no wish to do so, that I was afraid that washing myself might cause me to lose some of the Divine powers I had gained.

'Come on, son, you know this stuff's all a load o' rubbish, don't ya? Someone's just been telling you this when you've been caned some time and you're gettin' a flashback,' suggested the young man. There it was again. Flashback.

'Caned? You mean drunk, right?'

'Nor man. Anyway, get yourself in the bath.'

'No.'

'Right, then I'll get Wilma.' He disappeared for a moment and returned with Wilma, her face worn and scowling, her hair slightly more bushy than the previous day. She ran her hand into the warm water of the bath and pushed at my arm.

'Wilma, *warum muß ich wasche mich?*' I protested.

'*Man muß immer sich waschen. Es ist gut fur dein Gesundheit. Gehe bitte ins Bad.*' I decided to do as she said. Even in her native tongue she was pushy. Still, it was worth a try. I ran the soap over my body, hoping I was not washing away anything other than dirt.

After my bath, I asked if I might borrow a razor to shave, to which the answer was yes on the condition that Charlie do the shaving. He missed a few patches, and I complained and asked him to shave the areas he had missed. I could not understand why I was not allowed to do it myself, but he was patient with me. And then I dried, brushed my teeth and dressed.

Downstairs, breakfast had already begun. I listened to Charlie and Katie talking about the mysterious world of Middlesbrough night-clubs while I gobbled down my bacon and egg.

'Did you go to the Empire last Friday? Healy was on, wasn't he?'

'Aye. He's a bit overrated like, but I went. Prefer Judge Jules meself, he's more skilful, better with the crowd and that.' Charlie spoke quickly in a streetwise Middlesbrough accent, his small blue eyes shining back at Katie with interest.

'Oh, I really wanted to go. I think Healy's great. How about the Arena then?'

'The Arena? Yer bloody jokin' aren't ye?' Katie laughed at him. 'No! I saw Oasis there two year ago. Ye see some great new bands there on a Saturday night. Empire – Friday, Arena – Saturday, that's the way we always do it,' said Katie. I could see it already, Charlie going to the Arena in the future to see Katie, Katie boyfriendless and ready, surprised and delighted to meet him there.

I poured some tea. Tender Earthly Awareness. That's what I had. That's what tea enabled mankind to achieve. I took the tablets Wilma gave me. Looking to my right, I watched Catherine intent upon something in the air in front of her, painfully slow as usual. My eyes began to fixate on a poster on the wall beyond her. It was some medical poster, the writing too distant to read, featuring a large figure made of metal foil, the shape of a gent's toilet symbol. My red shirt reflected in the foil, and as I moved I saw the tint of my face reflecting back at me. The metallic nature of the figure intrigued me. The reflection was distorted, though I could just make out one of my dark eyes as I moved around in it.

I saw no one else reflecting in the poster. I was special, singled out. Recognised by higher powers. I shone, like the figure in the poster.

'Tender Earthly Awareness,' I said, interrupting Katie and Charlie's conversation.

'What?' Katie asked, her voice a little annoyed. So she did like him.

'Tea – that's what it stands for, Tender Earthly Awareness. Didn't you know? Drinking it is a tender activity between friends. And in doing so you gain a greater earthly awareness.' Charlie looked at Katie and the two of them started laughing hilariously.

'He's brilliant isn't he! I told 'im yesterday, I've been waiting for someone to make me laugh. Everything he does is so weird.'

'Aye, 'e's a daft un like, isn't he? But aye, I've never really been bothered about Club M – it's too expensive, like ...'

I was well and truly excluded. Too young for them. And maybe too wise. Singled out. Special. They were unaware of the great visionary in their presence, the one who would help save the world and lead it into the Golden Age. I sipped my tea.

This time Charlie and Katie washed up. I was told to stand behind them, like an extra on a film set. They were content to chat away, seeming oblivious to my presence. When we eventually moved to the lounge I picked up a cue and practised pool alone, as they sat and chatted some more. I had become a ghost.

Later that day, as Tim replaced Charlie, and I took satisfaction in beating the red-faced man at pool, a middle-aged woman with a pale face and shoulder-length dark brown hair stood in the doorway.

'Hi, James!' she said, in a tone that was familiar. But her face was not. Tim went to talk to the woman and I sat down to talk to Katie.

'You like Charlie, don't you?'

'He's alright. I used to go out with his brother, but we split up a couple of years ago. It's the first time I've had a chance to talk to 'im since I got 'ere. He's funny.' She remained distant, vaguely concentrating on a TV lunchtime quiz show.

Presently the woman with dark hair and eyes that were similar to my own came and sat next to me and hugged me. 'How are you?' she asked.

'Fine. Who are you, anyway? I sort of recognise your voice, but I don't remember meeting you. I'm busy talking to Katie.' The woman gave a sudden, low sob.

'Hi, Katie,' she said, trying to smile. Then she shook me slightly, her hands on my shoulders. 'Look, I'm your mother. I don't think you know what you're doing, do you? Poor lad.' I looked at her. She was strange. Evidently one of the ward's sicker patients. She wiped away a tear. 'Look, Tim and I need to take you for your scan now. Come on.'

Tim smiled stupidly at me as I got up. We walked out of the lounge, then paused at the front door while the big man's shaky hands fiddled with the lock. We stepped out into the frosty air. I shivered and saw my chance and ran as fast as I could for the hospital gate. I tried frantically to make my legs move quicker, but they were heavy and tired. I felt as though I was running through waist-high water. Running through the sea, trying to save a drowning friend.

The lumbering, out-of-breath Tim caught up with me eventually, and I was only half-way to the gate. His hands were rough, his fingers pinching my biceps like a crab's claws. Feeling like Cool Hand Luke, I was led to a waiting car, a white Peugeot 106, the brown haired woman already behind the wheel. She asked Tim for directions.

'Oh, it's – er – yeah, if you go left onto the road, it's the third – no the – er ... That's it, the second turn-off on your left, love.' The woman was not impressed.

'Ri – *ght*,' she said, examining him circumspectly through her dark eyes. I had begun to like her, whether she was crazy or not.

The woman turned the car left at the main road, then took the second turning on the left. We parked outside a large hospital building. Tim escorted us in, then to an elevator which took us up to the second floor. When the doors opened the smell of antiseptic flooded my nostrils, a doctor with snowy white hair awaiting us. He took us into a large room decorated in light blue, with a large frosted glass window to our left as we walked in. A machine that had a headset with electrodes plugged into it lay opposite the door, and was connected to a computer. It was just as I had imagined. They were going to examine me, to test my Divine powers. I remembered Steven Spielberg's *E.T.* and films about the life of Jesus, images of people refusing to believe, to accept things for what they were, to let things be.

'I think we can manage now,' the dark-haired woman said to Tim, 'I think he's a bit frightened of you. It'd be better if you waited outside. I want to make sure this test gets done properly.' Tim agreed, though somewhat reluctantly, and trudged back into the corridor.

The snowy-haired doctor took me to a reclining black leather chair beside the machine, and placed the headset on me, an electrode on each of my temples with two or three more tightly grasping the upper areas of my skull. He then stood back and exchanged a few murmured words with the dark-haired woman. A pretty young blonde woman then entered the room and smiled at the doctor. She sat down in a chair beside me, and briskly pressed a few keys on her computer.

'Now just relax. This won't take long.' She spoke in a smooth, calming tone. Her hair was done up in a neat ponytail. She had pale-blue eyes that were full of clarity and intelligence.

I lay back and expected a throbbing sensation, but there was no pain and no electric shocks. The blonde continued to soothe me, typing things into her computer. I closed my eyes and drifted into sleep, thinking of her.

When I awoke the brunette woman stood smiling over me, and the blonde had left the room.

'There, James, that wasn't too bad was it?' she asked. The white-haired doctor re-entered and spoke in hushed tones with the woman in a far corner of the room. He then removed the headset and I followed the woman out of the room as she thanked the doctor and wished him goodbye.

Tim sparked back to life as the door banged shut, jumping suddenly from a slumped position against the wall, his eyes tired and bloodshot.

'Right – erm. Shall we get goin' to the car then? I'll direct ye back.'

'You look like you've had a rough night,' the woman said.

'Aye, well you could say that,' Tim agreed.

Back at the Roseberry Centre, the woman came inside with me, then opened out her arms. I was tired of this game. I frowned and marched back into the lounge.

'He thinks I'm leaving him here on purpose,' I heard her say. I ignored the comment.

The day had turned dull, the sky a consistent grey colour like the ceiling of a prison cell. I watched Katie smoking, collecting the smoke into her lungs and holding it there with her eyes closed, her head falling heavily forward on to her chest as though it were concrete, bluish smoke escaping her lips.

In the lounge, a young boy of around ten or eleven was masturbating in a corner, his limp member unresponsive, eyes tight shut, his short ginger hair gelled forward. He had thrown his Manchester United top on the floor. I looked around at the other kids for help and when they noticed me doing so they shook their heads slowly. What was happening? I ran around the pool table. Tim entered and told me to stop, and when he did so I snagged my left leg into its corners, smiling defiantly back. Someone had to do something. People were suffering. I completed 12 laps of the table. The disciples must be recalled.

Katie re-entered, having chain-smoked two cigarettes. She sighed and took off her jacket, waved to me and left the room. I walked quickly down the corridor to talk to her, but was prevented by Tim, his large arms grabbing me.

'You wouldn't like it if I followed you around all the time, would yer?' he said, his bloodshot eyes staring threateningly back.

'But you do.'

'Yeah, but it's only for your own safety.'

'Oh, fuck off. This is a shit-hole. You're all shits.'

'What, Katie too?'

'No. I mean you people that run this place. You're shits. You let that young lad humiliate himself just then, DIDN'T YOU!' I shouted out the words. 'God will curse you at the Day of Judgement. You will be NOTHING!' Tim looked slightly afraid, then his fear turned into terrifying anger, his eyes widening, his teeth showing.

'Now look, *you*,' he said in a growling whisper, 'we are trying to help you. You're not well.'

'Don't you tell me *I'm* not well. *You're* the one who is not well,' I said, tapping my forefinger into his chest. He grabbed my arms, and turned me around.

'Just get back in there and behave, alright! You're just tryin' to be clever. And don't swear!'

I laughed. It felt exhilarating to raise my voice. Anyway, it had worked. Everyone in the lounge looked more cheerful now, and the boy with the ginger hair was now sitting in perfect calm, watching TV in his Manchester United top. The 12 disciples had worked their goodness in the room at my request. Katie was getting out her paints and brushes. She must have passed us in the corridor when we were arguing.

I went over and sat on a couch, pleased that Tim was now sitting and staring at the floor, his head down. It was time for him to know what it felt like. Katie was mixing various hues of red paint together, until she had created a deep maroon. I remembered that red from somewhere. I gazed and gazed at it, trying to catch up with some transitory memory. The colour seemed to speak to me in sad tones, to evoke feelings of both elation and ineptitude in a single moment ...

* * *

It was her favourite colour. As I walked into the bar of the country club, I waved to a distant cousin dancing beneath the kaleidoscope, her long fair hair and fifteen-year-old figure silhouetted by the rapidly changing colours. She didn't see me, and as usual was one of the first to be up there dancing. Only five or six dancing, not many more by the bar. And there she was.

There she was in her dark red velvet dress. She drank from a matching glass of what would probably be blackcurrant juice, as ID was required, and I knew she didn't have one. I stood for a moment looking at her, unaware that I had arrived, her dark-blue eyes surveying the party landscape, looking at all the people she did not know. The dark red went with her wavy fair hair beautifully, her eyes a seductive contrast. I was nervous now, but walked over none the less, smoothing my hair at the back with the palm of my right hand, trying to act with maturity and disguise my clumsiness.

'Hi, James!' she exclaimed, as though she had thought I was not coming.

'Hi Rachel! You look lovely.'

'So do *you*! And it's so nice to see you.' I thought about kissing her as she pouted slightly, but was unsure whether she would like that or not. It was only the third time we'd met and all of that was usually done at the end of the night. I was a bit shy with girls. I remembered kissing her two weeks before on the stairs of a hotel, both of us blind drunk.

'Yes, it's great to see you. Writing letters and talking on the phone's great, but it's not the same as seeing you in the flesh. I love your dress, by the way! I remember you mentioning it in your letter.'

'Ah, yes, the letter. I'm not very good at writing letters, I'm afraid. Your letters are *marvellous*. How do you think of enough things to write such long letters? And the poem you wrote for me was beautiful.' There was something that sounded too rehearsed in all of this.

'Oh, I've always written a lot. Anyway, I like writing to you. I feel we have some sort of understanding. I meant everything I said in the poem you know ...' I remarked nervously.

She looked at me a moment, the light from the bar flashing in the dark sea-blue eyes that had attracted me to her over a month before. She was serious, then smiled suddenly. 'I'd like a drink, wouldn't you?'

'Oh, yes – sorry, I forgot all about it! What do you want?'

'I'll have a Taboo and lemonade, please,' she said.

I was tense, and began worrying that I would be refused alcohol for being underage. Then I would feel I had let her down through my incompetence. Moreover, there was something about her that suggested her mind was elsewhere. Maybe she wasn't interested, but then that would come as no surprise. I hadn't had a proper girlfriend yet, and was sweet 16 already.

The bar had filled up quite a bit since Rachel and I had begun talking. When I finally turned around to hand over her Taboo and lemonade, I found she had drifted over to the stair-case on the other side of the bar. She was with the Yarm School bunch, most of whom I disliked or was disliked by. Furthermore her hand was on Giles Walder's inner thigh as she stood close to him, looking in his eyes, his hand on her bum. I took a large swig of cider and looked away.

* * *

Katie put her glass of water on the table with a bang.

'Don't you like that colour then? You look so sad, that's all,' she said.

'Oh, you know. Psychologists say colours give access to memory, don't they?'

'Oh, yeah, I read somethin' about that the other day. They did some random tests on people recently, didn't they, to prove it?'

'Yeah,' I looked at the fish still chasing each other out of their territories, every few minutes forgetting they had done so. 'I think I'd rather be a fish.'

8

Before dinner I failed to concentrate on *Byker Grove*, and paced rapidly about the room. I picked out a book at random from the bookshelf and was horrified to find that it and most of the others were dull best sellers. I couldn't find anything to stimulate me, as Katie and the rest were watching TV and shouted at me whenever I talked. I ran as fast as I could down the corridor to the base of the stairs, feeling as though I had superhuman energy levels. The narrow corridor breezed the air briskly through my ears like an alpine wind. At the base of the wooden stairs I paused, and realising Tim must have nodded off again, I treaded carefully up them.

At the top I tried to remember the pin number, but it was no use. A red light kept coming on when I typed in each incorrect attempt, so I decided to give up. I went to the toilet beside the foot of the stairs. All I'd wanted was to go to my room. I was tired of having to be social and wanted peace and quiet. As I looked up from the urinal, the light sparkled in the frosted glass window above me like various piles of precious gems, blue stacked upon white, stacked upon green. What a wealth of wonder lay in all these small things so often overlooked.

I ran my left hand rapidly through the cold tap 12 times, then did the same with my right. Then I turned on the hot water tap and did the same again. Hot and cold in equal measure, 24 hours a day. Dark and light. It was the most one could hope for. I hoped to restore man's equilibrium through the influence of these symbolic tasks. These things would all have a cumulative effect for the betterment of the world.

I walked from the toilet and investigated the kitchen and dining-room, finding nothing of interest on their surfaces, not wanting to rummage around in the cupboards. Walking quickly past the doorway of the lounge I turned right toward the office, which was shut. I was curious. Turning the handle as slowly as I could so as not to arouse suspicion, I pushed it, and the door miraculously opened. They had forgotten to lock it! Excited, I closed the door carefully behind me and began to look through the filing cabinets for clues about where I was, and why I was here.

Suddenly, I found a file, 'JAMES FOUNTAIN' at its edge in bold type. I pulled it out and set it on the desk reading Dr Anderson's conservative scrawl:

6.2.96   Arranged transfer from Hartlepool.
           Thoughts racing, no sleep. 'Seen the light.'

           Perplexed, preoccupied, vague stare ...
           Av. build, dark hair.
           Glasses.
           Acne.
           Casual clothes, staring straight ahead.
           Hypomanic and somatic s/s.
           Thoughts – disordered.
           Not suicidal.
     Mother reports a sudden change when he went out to a
        party.
     Otherwise high achiever – good academic...

'WHAT DO YOU THINK YOU'RE DOING!' Tim stood in the doorway, almost triumphant in his sudden obligation to be furious with me. 'Get out!' he snarled, grabbing me by the hair and flinging me from the room.

'Ah, but you're too late!' I yelled. 'I know what you're all up to. You *are* testing me. You're keeping me here illegallyunderthefalsepretencethatI'mill!'

'Sorry, Mr Berkeley, you'll have to speak more slowly and

clearly if you want me to reply. That's too bloody quick that is.'

I gave up. But from the way Tim called me 'Berkeley' I realised they'd been talking amongst themselves about my failed attempt to crack the code. Great. And now nobody could understand me. I was too fast for them.

I marched into the lounge, happy to have had a brief period of escape. So it was possible to break the so-called 'rules'. I was glad of this knowledge and that finally I had proof I was not losing my senses. They were checking up on a young man whose future was uncertain, but whose genius was undeniable. He was evidently destined for great things, to do things that would benefit mankind, though they did not yet know what. Dr Anderson had written 'seen the light', 'high achiever', 'good academic'. They recognised the potential in me. This E.E.G. was to be the first in a series of tests. They were trying pills on me in order to direct and channel my performance, just as top athletes were put on programmes of isotonic consumption and diets.

I bounced towards the couches on which Katie and the others sat as if I was walking on the moon. As I moved around in a state of ecstasy, thoughts came hurtling toward me with tremendous force. It was all becoming apparent: Europe needed to bind together – a single currency, a single presidency, a single language. Every continent needed to become one in order that people could redeem themselves before the Day of Judgement in 2000AD. Only through a quashing of all violent and criminal activity – both politically and socially motivated – could the world be made ready for the four horsemen of the Apocalypse. I remembered the priest's sermon from the *Book of Revelation* at school some weeks ago. I remained standing in the middle of the room looking through the window, stroking the light stubble on my chin.

'What are you thinking about, James?' asked a soft voice close by me.

'Eurovision' I said quietly, not wanting everyone to hear. I realised the voice belonged to Katie, her hand on my shoulder.

'What? What did you say? Oh, you look so happy and peaceful! I wish I could find something similar. I'm miserable, James. I'm bored.'

'Don't be. Because Eurovision will change the world. It will instil a unifying bond among mankind! It will light the road to goodness!' The blood roared around my veins at the speed of a Japanese bullet train. I lifted my head and opened my eyes wide, stretched out my arms.

'Eurovision? You mean that God-awful song contest? Or that single currency business?'

'No! Eurovision means one vision for Europe, one way of seeing things. The same would apply for Australasia, Asia, America and Africa. It is the simplest way to rid the world of poverty, crime and violence. This is why God created five continents in the first place, to make it easier to control these problems. But now, four years before Judgement Day, the disciples are being recalled. One for every sign of the zodiac, one for every month of the year. Jesus will rise again.'

'And what is your role in all of this?' Katie asked. I was confused by her question. I paced back and forth for a few minutes, rapt in intense concentration. And then I had it. Of course.

'I am the disciple James. St James. It is my job to help contact and recall the other disciples.' And then, all of a sudden, I cried 'EUROVISION!' as loud as I could. All of the patients, the various nurses whom I kept forgetting were not patients but who were assigned to look after various patients on an individual basis – among them Tim – looked up in bewilderment from the latest episode of *Neighbours*. Wilma came with another tablet.

'No, I won't take it. I saw the notes. You're trying to poison me, you've got me here for testing.'

'Poison you? You're not making much sense, James. And

you're frightening ze other patients. Please take zis to calm you down.'

'Wilma, I am perfectly calm. Besides, you are in no position to judge *my* condition.'

'James, just take it, it would be easier.'

'What is it, anyway? You've never told me what's in these things before!'

'This is Procyclidine. It's to relax you.'

'It looks too big. Maybe I'll take a smaller one.'

'This is the smallest size, 5 mg. But maybe you vant me to halve it?'

I decided I could take it. If I was St James, nothing was beyond my constitution. I could take anything.

I grabbed the glass of water and swallowed the pill, its chalky aftertaste making me retch. Wilma heaved an audible sigh of relief, then trudged back to the kitchen where she was no doubt preparing the evening meal. Katie stared at me from the couch, then turned back to the TV. The others giggled and talked amongst themselves, the various nurses calming them. Judith walked slowly past in her purple jumper, looking at me strangely from behind her black eyeshadow.

'You never talk to me,' she whispered, drifting out of the room.

A few minutes later, looking through the patio door, planning how I would escape if I could only break through the glass, I saw the reflection of a beautiful but very thin girl at the threshold of the room. As I turned around her olive eyes looked back at me, then they flashed around the room in sudden glances. Her black hair was tied in a neat bun at the back. The appearance of her harrowing figure brought with it an atmosphere of pity.

'Eee, look at this! Downstairs for the first time in two days!' said Tim.

'Hi, Annette, you alright, petal?' Katie asked gently, standing and running both of her hands slowly across

Annette's head and kissing her cheek.

'Yeah, a bit better thanks. Cheers for the sandwiches,' said Annette, speaking in warm, quiet tones. 'I see someone else has arrived.'

'Oh, yes, that's James,' she lowered her voice slightly, 'he's a bit strange but very nice, you know.' I stood looking out of the window pretending not to listen. I had been curious what Katie thought about me. 'James! Come and meet Annette.'

I walked across, feeling like God's special gift to women. Maybe it was one of the temptations that went along with being a saint – lots of bright-eyed concubines about. I was in demand. I shook Annette's hand and sat down on a sofa with Katie and her. Everyone else was getting up.

'You comin' to dinner?' Katie asked Annette,

'No, Wilma's already given me some soup. I can't take too many solids right now. My stomach's fragile.'

'Annette goes to a private school too, James. Polam Hall wasn't it, Annie?'

'Yes. Until I was sick a few months ago. You like Yarm?' she asked me. Deep craters had been sunk beneath her eyes. Her hands were bony and shaking. I considered her question.

'I like some of the teachers. But I don't have many friends. I suppose I'm different.'

'Yes, I'm the same. They all think they're supermodels with their flashy designer clothes and make-up. They made me feel ugly and then I lost too much weight.' Annette was well-spoken with a heartbreaking hint of self-deprecation in her voice. Tim was coming over.

'Right, let's 'ave y'all in the dinin' room. Except of course you, Annette. She's 'ad her breadcrumbs, 'aven't ye, pet!' He smiled. He was just teasing her, and for the first time I warmed to him. 'Eh, that tablet worked didn't it, son? Normally ye'd've 'ad a go at me by now!'

As I walked along the corridor to the dining room I once

73

again shouted 'EUROVISION!' as loud as I could. I felt sad for Annette, her pale face a haunting contrast to her jet-black hair, her eyes so beautiful there seemed no justification for any kind of suffering to be going on behind them. Eurovision would solve all that. She would be one of those healed on Christ's return.

As I sat down at the usual table with Katie and Tim, I decided I would follow Jesus' example. I divided my food in half, leaving two fish fingers and half my chips for the rest of the world. It could be divided up, as Jesus had at the feeding of the five thousand.

'What are ye doin'? An' remember to take yer tablets.' Tim stared at my plate, and I swallowed the tablets that lay as usual next to my mealtime water. I looked at the metallic poster to my right, the colour red reflecting from my shirt. I represented world aid, I was to heal the whole world one by one, it was my ordained responsibility, along with the rest of the disciples. The poster was a reminder, like the branch that had been tapping at my window the previous night.

After she realised I'd left half of my food, Wilma came back with my plate .

'You're getting too sin, James. You don't vant to end up like Annette, do you?'

'Nein ich bin sehr gut, danke. Ich mochte gern Annette hilfen.'

'Why are you speaking in German? We are in Inkland. And do you really think someone like you can help Annette? You can't even help yourself. Your face is sinner every day, you are not eating enough.'

'Annette is my responsibility. The health of the world is my responsibility. Take a look at that poster.' I pointed to my right. 'I'm the only one who reflects in it, and that means I've been chosen.'

'I see no reflection. It's your imagination, James. You did take your tablets, ja?'

'Ja, danke.'

'Zen eat up your food. Tim!' She made steady eye contact with him. Katie seemed to have lost interest in her food, and was absentmindedly cutting her fish fingers and chips into tiny pieces.

'Annette's really sick, James,' she said. 'You can't do anything for her.'

'Yes I can. You don't understand.' I sat with my head in my hands.

'It's a nice thought, but she's been 'ere four months now, and she's not gettin' any better. The best you can do is talk to her like I do and be her friend.'

'Well, exactly – that's one way in which Divine powers work,' I said, glad the message was finding a way through. Katie mashed her food together with her fork.

'It's just not fair. She might never get out of here.'

'Nor will you or Mr Berkeley unless you eat yer food up! It's gettin' late, ya know!' barked Tim.

'You're a bastard, d'you know that?' Katie snapped.

Later, I tried to cheer Katie up by singing Oasis songs to her as we washed up, twisting the words in order to irritate Tim.

'So Tim is a shit,
He knows that he is as we're walkin' on by,
His soul's far from great, but don't look back in anger
I heard you say.'

'I heard *you* say, James!' We laughed together. It felt good to have a soulmate, to have a common adversity. Tim's face boiled red, but he did not shout. One of my darker theories was that Tim fancied Katie in some perverse way. He leaned quite close to her at times in conversation, and she would lean away.

'Anyway, Charlie's comin' back tomorrow. He can try and look after ye's.'

'Oooh, getting all emotional are we?' Katie smiled brightly at me, and I smiled too, but gestured that maybe we had better stop teasing him. After all, he was a big man.

Eastenders was particularly irritating that night, but I was outvoted in my wish to change the channel. Grant Mitchell was having some petty argument with his brother Phil. Someone said they'd heard Grant would be killed off in a few months and I was glad. I looked at Tim and decided he looked a bit like the kid Ricky, but a bit fatter and redder in the face. Whenever the ginger-haired Bianca moaned at her boyfriend Judith would imitate her.

'Wick-e-ey!' Everyone laughed. I made sure she saw me laughing, hoping this would help to make up for my recent neglect of her. She smiled back, all forgiven. I turned to Tim and tried to impersonate Bianca myself. But neither he nor anyone else saw the point of the joke, so I laughed alone.

At eight o'clock the nurses changed over, after a short meeting in the office. Terry came into the lounge with his big, bushy moustache, still wearing the black woolly hat he used to guard his hairless head against the February cold. The other nurses hung about in the office, chatting. It seems they didn't want to spend more time than necessary with the patients, preferring to sit outside their doors. The cold air had steadily made itself felt from the recently closed front door. I shivered slightly.

'Eee, you don't wanna go out there, son. It's bloody freezin'. I'll be glad when spring's 'ere.' His talk depressed me.

'You've no idea how much I want to go out there,' I said.

Soon we were escorted to bed. I lay in the dark for a long time, watching the same man sitting in the doorway as the previous night, turning over the pages of his Wilbur Smith paperback. Meanwhile I tried to work out who the other 12 disciples might be. Were they all the same age as myself? Or were they a range of ages, from a range of cities and countries around the world? But soon exhaustion gripped my eyelids, as though someone were using pliers to tug them down. I gave in, and began rolling down a never-ending tunnel towards sleep.

9

When I awoke it was still dark, and from the moment my eyes opened I felt fearful. There was a vacuousness in the searching gaze of the man in the doorway, hollow and uncompromising. There were to be no surprises in this place, no excitements. There had simply been some misunderstanding, and I was misunderstanding's victim. As I stared at the ceiling spiralling higher above me as I watched, I envisaged the possibility that I was wrong, and that no God would ever answer my cries for help, that the empty heavens would simply stand by and witness the ending of another tragic life. Everything would carry on as normal ... I would just be imprisoned here until I took my own life, and there would be nothing more to be said.

I thought of Annette and her poor, thinning body and beautiful sad eyes. I thought of Katie and her moments of disillusion, mashing her food slowly, painting in bright primary colours. I heard screams of pain nearby, howls of anguish and misery, which came to an abrupt end as someone woke out of a nightmare. The person's breathing then steadied itself as he or she settled back into sleep. I imagined it was probably Katie. She was sure to be the sort who experienced nightmares. Probably from worrying about Annette so much. I wanted to hold them both close, to tell them it would all be OK, to whisper comforting words. But the words would not have been spoken with any conviction.

Soon I heard someone else screaming. I gazed at the orange glow of the street lamp, trying to be calm, to endure the audible onslaught of suffering. I transferred my gaze to the man in the chair focussed indifferently on his book, unfazed by the external projections of inner pain. To him it would just seem like some horror movie in the background, from a TV he had forgotten to switch off. I remembered the look of his lifeless, unresponsive eyes up close, and felt afraid. The world had stopped caring.

After the silent, anticipatory moment that is the prelude to dawn, daylight began creeping its way into the room. I lay, eyes wide, waiting for the next scream. But it never came, and the thin song of a blackbird was all that pierced the silence.

I noticed Charlie had taken up his position in my doorway. He winked at me, so I turned away and lay facing the wall for a considerable period of time. I wanted to end it all. The blackbird seemed to speak to me through his whining lament, to say that another day was here, and to ask whether it mattered. My bed felt like a grave, and I was heavy within it, enshrined as I was in this place, an appropriate end for a saint. The blackbird sang a few final notes of encouragement, his little head rotating round to look at me looking back at him through the parting of the curtains, then flew away.

Charlie came to get me up soon after the bird's departure, and my knee joints cracked loudly as I stood and stretched.

'Sleep much?' he asked.

'A little. Not much.'

'Eh, you'll be alright soon, lad. Don't let it get you down.'

After washing and dressing, I went downstairs with Charlie and began my breakfast, which was waiting for me. I watched crows sitting in the small tree outside the breakfast room window, their dark shapes nightmarish against the white sky. I imagined the carcasses of dead animals they would have eaten for breakfast. They collected up the rotting leftovers of the world. If no one else found my dead body in a field, then they surely would. Nature allowed nothing to go to waste.

Katie came downstairs, looking half-asleep.

'Hi, Charlie! Hi, James.'

'Hi,' I returned flatly. I didn't want to see her. I didn't want to see anybody. I sat looking at my empty plate with resignation. Outside, the crows were picking something from their claws.

'How come you're still wearing that red shirt? Don't you want to change your clothes now and then?' Katie asked me.

'I don't really care to be honest. What does it matter?'

'What do you mean? Of course it matters. Charlie, get him a clean shirt, will you. He's been wearing that one for three days.'

'I don't see the point. May as well save the washing. I'll be buried here soon.'

'Shut up! You'll be out in a couple of weeks. They don't keep you here forever.'

'Maybe not you. But because I'm a saint they'll bury me here, to bless the place. I'm in a tomb.'

Katie shook her head and took a bite of toast, and Charlie grabbed my arm and took me upstairs. He selected a fresh shirt from my wardrobe, chequered green and white, and I put it on, shaking my head.

To my surprise, Charlie took me through to the lounge. I thought he would be wanting to speak to Katie. As we were the first to go in there, I turned on the TV and flicked through the channels. I was pleased to find an episode of *Tom and Jerry*, and settled back on the couch. I could hear Charlie practising pool shots, cursing to himself whenever a shot went astray. Tom was chasing Jerry with a fly swatter, Jerry evading it each time and then finding a needle. As he jammed it into Tom's backside, something in me broke, and I began to gush forth laughter as I fixated on the image of Tom's pain-stricken face, seeming to catch him in slow motion as his body leapt into the air and his head stuck in the ceiling.

Though conscious of my laughter becoming slightly maniacal, I couldn't stop, and nor did I particularly care. As Tom's body wriggled to break his head free from the ceiling, I laughed and laughed and laughed. I was completely oblivious to any other activity in the room. Nothing visible or audible could break through the riot of hilarity ripping through me, my eyes screwed up, my stomach muscles in considerable pain now as I laughed rapidly, on and on. Eventually I heard people shouting, and I slowed and quietened, realising that the shouting was aimed at me. Judith sat opposite, shouting from behind a magazine, Charlie yelling from the far end of the room looking ready to fling his pool cue in my direction. Katie was stood in the centre of the room, an incredulous, half-smiling, half-frowning expression across her face. I sat back exhausted, holding my stomach. There was a collective sigh of relief.

The cartoon was over too, and now Jerry Springer was pacing back and forth across the screen, his left arm across his chest, his right hand upon his craggy chin, a pretty young black woman crying and moaning that she knew her man was sleeping with another woman. I got up and wandered about the room, restless and agitated. I took off my glasses so as to avoid catching the disbelieving glances being shot in my direction from Charlie, Katie and co.

Soon I saw the tall figure of Dr Anderson in the doorway.

'James, will you come through, please?' I took my glasses from the side of the pool table and put them on, following Dr Anderson down to the office. She closed the door. 'So. How do you feel today?' I settled slowly into my chair, my knees clicking as I did so. I looked at the desk.

'OK.'

'And what does "OK" mean? Are your thoughts still racing?'

'Yes. They make me feel tired. I lie in bed at night waiting for them to go away, but they never do.'

'You sound a bit more depressed than before. Is that why?'

'I'm tired of these thoughts. I can feel myself dying here slowly.' My gaze would not shift from the desk. Dr Anderson was one of the people keeping me here, after all. 'I know you'll never let me leave. And if you don't I'll kill myself.'

'Of course we'll let you leave when you're better. But you're not well.'

'Then what's wrong with me?'

'I don't know. We're waiting for some results to come back to give us a clearer picture. But it seems that you have some sort of drug-induced mania. A blood sample was taken at Hartlepool General which should tell us which drugs are in your system. Something must have happened to you at this party you went to. Can you remember any more about that yet?'

'No. Just that I saw other people taking drugs, just like any party, I guess. I went off into the wilderness with my friend Julian Welsh and we talked about the future, and when I came back I saw people dealing stuff from a van, taking money. I remember someone warning me the day before that there was a chance of being spiked at Hardwick Hall, that he'd heard it had happened to someone before, that I should watch out. So I felt quite protective towards my friends, wanted to warn them about it.'

'So you are starting to remember more, that's good. Could you look into my eyes when you speak?'

'What's the point? You're all keeping me here for something. Why can't I go home?'

'So you remember your family now? Your mother tells me you didn't recognise her yesterday.'

'My mother? She wasn't here yesterday.'

'She took you for your E. E. G. scan.'

'No, I don't remember her being here.'

Dr Anderson was jotting down notes again. 'OK ... about your thoughts. What are you thinking about most of the time?'

'About God, and what he wants me to do.'

'And you feel that God controls you?'

'No ... it's more that he guides me. But then the Devil has a say in it all, just as he does with everybody. I have to use my own will to stay with God, to stay alive for him.'

'And what do you think God wants you to do?'

'I am St James. I have a responsibility to look after people. I received a vision from God, as I told you, and I need to tell the world all about it. But like anybody, my will to live is sometimes diminished. SucharethepressuresI'mputunderhere … confined with people I have never met … not allowed to go to school. I'm supposed to be going on a school skiing trip this weekend, to see the world from on high, to be given a greater plane of view, as God intended. This is vital for the future of mankind. But I'm sure you'll stop me from going on that as well. You've just put this down to some spiked drink. You don't understand, like the rest of them.'

'I can't make out all the words you are saying. Your speech is hurried and unclear at times. So, yes you are in no fit state to return to school. But you must understand that we have no wish to keep you here any longer than necessary. Do you agree to stay until you are better?' She spoke so convincingly that for a moment I believed she was right, that I was not my normal self.

'Yes, I'll stay for a little while. But I need to do my exams, so I can't stay long. My work cannot be put off forever.'

'We are hopeful that you won't need to stay long.' Dr Anderson jotted down some hurried notes. I wondered whether she had learned of my discovery of the file the previous day. 'Can you tell me today's date, please?'

'It's the ninth of February, nineteen ninety-seven.'

'Interesting. And the time?'

'About lunch time.'

'Do you know where we are?'

'At a university, which is carrying out research on remarkable people.' I remembered Katie's artwork. 'Or maybe you're nurturing young talent.'

The doctor took off her glasses and leaned forward. 'Right, James, let me make it clear to you that you're in a hospital –'

I looked up from the desk for the first time. 'Yes, but you might just be saying that to record my reaction.'

'– and the year is 1996. Why did you say 1997?'

'It feels as if a year has gone by.'

Dr Anderson smiled and rose.

'I'll see you again soon, James.' I breathed a sigh of relief, stepping out of the door as she held it open, and went back into the lounge.

After lunch, I played a game of pool with Katie. She was on form today, beating me with ease, but striking the balls with a new and disturbing aggression. In between shots she rambled about a nightmare she had had during the night, which mostly consisted of some guy who used to be her boyfriend chasing after her with a knife. The description she gave was so vivid it caused me to envisage it cinematically before me. I felt like Macbeth, and remembered my English teacher some weeks ago talking to us about the Shakespearean character's hallucinatory imagination.

To my surprise, one of the members of that class suddenly entered the room, whom I immediately recognised to be my friend Julian Welsh.

'Julian, how are you, mate? Haven't seen you for ages!' It was a relief to see his cloud of brown hair and large, bright blue eyes.

'I know, it seems like that to me, too. So how's things?' Julian said.

'Oh, you know ...'

'Heya, Julian, I'm Katie,'

'Pleased to meet you,' said Julian. I could tell he fancied her. Julian seemed to fancy every girl he met.

'I'm just nippin' out for a fag, James. We'll finish off the game later.' Katie put down her cue and Julian followed me down to the far end of the room. We sat on the couches facing one another.

'Everyone's talking about you, James. They all want to know how you are.'

'I'm fine.'

'Really? I suppose you don't look too bad ... What's the

84

food like here?'

'Oh, it's alright. Not great.'

'Well, that's hospital, isn't it? The food's always shite.'

'So this is a hospital? I've been trying to work that out. They keep telling me it is, but I keep thinking they might be trying to test me.'

'Test you? ... Do you know what happened to you yet?' I looked at the fish tank. So that was it. Visits to see James in the goldfish bowl, a hot topic of conversation at school. Since when had I been hot gossip at school? I remembered the sign: 'Psychiatric Ward'.

'There were some hallucinations after I came back from the party. God sent me some visions. But now they reckon I'm on a trip or something.'

'Yes. They think someone spiked your drink with LSD.'

'Really?' I stared at him momentarily, tried to hold a transitory fragment of memory in my mind that escaped almost as quickly as it entered. 'How did they come to that conclusion?'

'Well, like you told me at the time, there was a lot of drugs there that night. You were saying someone warned you about being spiked the day before. And then Giles Walder took off with your girlfriend, didn't he? Rachel's really upset about it all, by the way. She feels really guilty ...'

'Good for her.' This was all too much to take in. 'What else do you know?'

'No more than that. The police are running some investigations.'

'Anyway this is all irrelevant. Doesn't everyone realise I've been sent a vision, a communication from God? Life will never be the same.'

Julian shook his head. He was a disbeliever. I gave up trying to convince him. He always was too rational for this kind of thing.

'Things'll be back to normal soon. And then you'll be back

85

doing the dreaded GCSEs and shit! And worrying about how crap Leeds are! You got beat 2–0 at home to Sheff Wed on Monday night!'

'Yeah, right. So Arsenal are still boring as usual are they? Still playing the long ball system like they did in the Dark Ages?' We laughed together, Julian protesting. 'You going skiing tomorrow then, you lucky bastard?'

'Oh, yeah. Sorry you can't come, that's really harsh. It won't be the same without you there. Still, there'll always be next year, I guess ...'

'Well, you could help me escape, then I could go with you, to see the world from on high as God intended!'

'No, I don't think I ...'

'Why not? We could go now ...' I thought of my previous failed attempts at escape and realised it was fantasy to suppose I could do it now. '... actually, I guess you're right. Anyway, it was good of you to come.'

'No problem. You'll be okay, though, won't you? You look terrible.'

'Thanks! You look like a sack of shit yourself. The truth is, until last night I hadn't slept since the party.'

'What? Fucking hell! Don't they give you sleeping tablets and stuff?'

'They give me tablets. But they don't seem to work sometimes.' I watched his lightly freckled, rational face. He was calm and still, with none of the panic about him I recognised in myself. It was like looking into an imaginary mirror and seeing the picture of health I used to be, staring back. Julian was 'normal' as Dr Anderson would say. The Yarm School boy. We were no longer on the same level. 'Julian, this place is a nightmare. Maybewhenyoucomeback ... Butprobablynotforawhile ... MaybeI'llkillmyselfbeforetheyletme.'

Julian leaned forward, his eyes screwed up, his nose turning up slightly, the way it always did when he didn't understand something in class.

'What? Sorry, I didn't understand half of that – you spoke too quickly.'

'Oh, just forget it. It's not important.' Perhaps suicide was the wrong thing to talk about to an old friend who'd come to visit. Anyway, I knew he wouldn't understand.

'I really hope you'll feel better soon. Everyone at school wants you to get better as quickly as possible.'

I found this difficult to believe. 'Really. Even those shits who used to beat me up and take the piss all the time? Come on, Ju! They'll be pleased I'm here, so they can laugh at me.'

Julian shook his head decisively. 'No, I don't think so. It's making them feel guilty. You'll see. Anyway, take care. Your mother's here to take me back to school.' The woman who had picked me up to take me for my scan came into the room, and now I realised this woman was my mother. I was unenthusiastic at the sight of her, and sat cross-legged, puzzled that I had not recognised her the day before.

'Hi, James! Have you had a nice time with Julian?'

'Yes, but now you're going to take him away, aren't you? And then you're going to leave me here to rot in this miserable place on my own. Do you know what it's like?'

'Oh, come on, darling, you've got to be positive.' She put her arms around me. I avoided her eyes. 'The doctor told me you're improving.'

'Really. I don't think that's true, do you?' I asked spitefully, looking blankly at the empty space where Julian had been sitting. My mother squeezed my shoulders, then left the room with Julian, crying, 'I'll be back tomorrow!' as the front door slammed shut.

I sat, trying to filter everything Julian had told me through my mind, which seemed to have shattered into fragments of various sizes. It felt as if I was attempting to reconstruct an ancient bowl, but I was a clumsy archaeologist, and the superglue of jealousy would get all over my fingers, hindering me from putting the whole artefact back together with any success.

Each time I felt it would hold water I would turn it around in my fingers to find a vital piece still missing, undermining its overall worth as memory.

I felt someone close by, and then I realised it was Katie.

'Hey! We've got a game of pool to finish 'ere James! Your mate's gone, hasn't he?'

'Yes ... Oh, sure ... let's finish it.'

'Cool.'

I watched Katie leaning over the table, her lithe, nimble body arching over with ease as she tapped in another red. But soon I was back there in the reconstruction process, and this time I felt the artefact held as much water as it had when first produced.

* * *

The cider was sweet, and I had asked for dry. No matter. Beggars can't be choosers I thought to myself, looking across the bar. Rachel had begun kissing Giles, the inevitable step from her hand on his leg and his hand on her bum. One was a mere step behind the other. Her fingers went through his stawberry blonde hair, and his went into hers until they looked like a grotesque, faceless animal moving in the half-light. Her beautiful sea-blue eyes were closed now, her face tipped upwards for him. She looked happier with him, sexier. I tried to avoid pathos, I tried not to feel.

I turned my back and drank some more cider, leaning against the bar. I watched the dance floor, and saw some people I'd met at a party over Christmas waving at me. I waved back half-heartedly, trying to smile. I looked up at the kaleidoscope swirling its myriad colours around like false hope, fake stars thrown carelessly against the ceiling from the giant silver ball. The music got louder and I felt myself steadily enclosed by a thumping wall of bass. Darkness descended as the lights dimmed so I stepped away from the bar and moved into its close embrace.

I walked around to the foot of the stairs. Giles was at the bar ordering drinks, Rachel stood behind, rocking to and fro, looking towards the dance floor, getting ready to dance. Going up the stairs I saw Manoj Sidhu and Jim Savage, their eyes lingering on the bar, their unmistakably tall, thin outlines leaning against the bannister.

'How did you get served, James?' said Jim, spotting the pint in my hand. 'They asked us for ID.'

'Just lucky I guess.'

'Wanna fag?' Manoj asked, waving his packet of Marlboro at me.

'No thanks.' I was not going to be bribed to get drinks for them. I did not class them as friends, more as former members of a cohort of bullies. I was finding it difficult to forgive them.

I walked along a narrow corridor, which opened out into a large, ornate room. Cigarettes winked at me like orange fireflies from couches situated around the dark fringes. At the far side was a balcony, which looked out over the dance floor. As my eyes adjusted, I saw Gaby Antrim smoking one of them, sitting with her usual bitch pal, Nicholas Gates. Gaby's bleached blonde hair gave her away, and as I looked, Nick's hair was outrageously over-correct as usual.

'Hey, Gaby, Nick. How's things?'

'Oh, alright. Can't bloody well get served, though. No one can. How come you 'ave anyway?' Gaby asked. As usual, her eyes were heavily caked in black eyeshadow and eyeliner, so that it seemed an effort for her to keep them open.

'Maybe it's because I got here early,' I said.

'We'll try again later. Let's go and see who's dancing.'

We walked over to the balcony and leaned over the edge examining the faces of the now heaving multitude. I watched flashing white lights whipping against features, which sometimes appeared bestial and desperate when captured by the brightness. In the staccato light I attempted to find someone I recognised, to help me through the chaos. Nights out like this were a novelty for me, but the norm for Gaby and Nick.

Julian Welsh came suddenly into view, drifting aimlessly around the edges of the dance floor, looking as hopelessly out of place as I felt. No doubt he had been talking to someone on the stairs and I had missed him. I finished my pint and placed it on a table behind me.

'I'm just going to talk to Julian,' I told Gaby and Nick, and set off towards the stairs to find him.

As I reached the bottom of the stairs I saw him slumped on the bar, trying to catch the barmaid's eye.

'Hey, Julian!' I said, jabbing him in the back with a knuckle. He turned round in fright.

'Jesus, you scared the shit out of me! How's it going, then? Not too good with Rachel I see,' he said, pointing towards the happy couple, merged together in the corner in a big leather chair.

'No. Not good. Can you get me a glass of lemonade when she serves you? I'm thirsty as hell.'

'No problem.'

I gave him 50p. I knew they wouldn't serve him alcohol anyway. Julian looked more like 14 than 16.

'So, what are you gonna do, twat him one? I would.'

'No you wouldn't!' I said laughing. 'Anyway, what's the point? He'd only beat the crap out of me like they all used to. I'm too soft for that kind of thing.'

'Maybe you're right.' We drank, Julian having miraculously got himself a pint. The lemonade was a welcome refreshment, the bubbles blasting around my mouth, rejuvenating me.

'Do you want to go outside when you've finished that?' I suggested. 'It's too warm in here.'

'Yeah, good idea.' Julian nodded, gulping down more lager.

We finished the drinks and skirted around the dance floor. Pushing past the bouncers, we went outside like deep sea divers coming up for air. The stars stared back at me, silver and serene through the black sky. A full moon guided us down the unlit drive, like two travellers who had forgotten where they were going.

'What do you think then – about all this?' I asked, not sure exactly what I was trying to ask.

'About all what?'

'Well ... where do you think we'll all end up?'

'Dunno ... I'll probably study law and work locally. You'll probably ... well, hopefully you'll become a writer. Your poetry's pretty good.'

'Well, good enough to win fifth place in our school creative writing competitions! I suppose you never know. But I think I'd like to become an academic in a university, you know? Continue to live in the great goldfish bowl we're in already at private school.' We laughed. But then I became serious. 'We don't really know what we're doing, do we? I mean how do we know what's going to happen in a place like this? We're not streetwise, we don't know how to take care of ourselves ...' I looked at Julian, who was looking downcast at the ground. 'Suppose I told you that yesterday at school I was warned someone might spike my drink?'

'By who?'

'Chris Taylor.'

'Well, he would know I suppose. He comes to these things all the time. But he's not here tonight is he?'

'No.'

'Ah, well ... my mum always tells me to watch my drink. You never know who wants to take you out of the picture at a party.'

'I suppose so. There must be a lot of E being done in there. I saw some people on the dance floor I knew ...'

'Oh, come on James, loads of people do it nowadays. I didn't think you cared what other people did.'

'No, I don't care about that. I'm just worried about what Chris said, that's all.'

Julian sighed, his breath turning into thick smoke, curling upward toward the stars. 'Let's go back in, I'm getting cold. Just forget it. And forget about Rachel, she's probably drunk or something.'

'You're right. Maybe all I need's another drink,' I said, trudging back down the drive with him. I couldn't help noticing a suspicious-looking white transit van parked outside. I felt very curious, despite Julian's assurances. I got out my notebook after he had re-entered the club and wrote down the numberplate. I would make my own enquiries, if no one else was going to. I folded up the notebook, returning it to my inside coat pocket, and followed my friend back in.

* * *

'James! James! Are you gonna take your shot or not?' I looked up and saw Katie looking back, frustrated.

'Oh, yes ... Sure ... What am I again?'

10

Llewellyn was a tall man with grey hair and a thin, craggy face. He walked into the lounge after dinner, and I got up and introduced myself. I felt certain that this rugged giant was the one I had been waiting for, who would transport me to the next stage of my Divine training. His withered-looking, sinewy features reminded me of Clint Eastwood. He clasped my open hand lightly.

'Do you want a game of pool?' I asked him.

'Aye, son, if you like.'

After I had split the pack, I decided to see if my intuition was correct.

'Where are you from?' I asked.

'I'm from Easterside, son. Middlesbrough.' Of course. I had mistaken the place name for Eastwood. This was Eastwood the man, come to take me to Westmoreland. I was excited, eager to get moving, but held myself in check.

'You are Eastwood, aren't you?' I whispered to him as I took another shot.

He smiled. 'Aye,' he winked, 'but don't tell anyone OK? If anyone knows I'm Clint I'll get mobbed!'

I smiled, but took this as a covering code. To me, he had just admitted he was Eastwood and everything was on for a secret transfer this evening. As he spoke, these codes echoed in my ears, and the words spoken aloud seemed dim in the background. I watched his clear, ageless sky-blue eyes focus upon another yellow and pot it cleanly into the middle of a pocket. He seemed focussed and precise, as I imagined God's agents would be, resolved.

Later that night, Llewellyn sat outside my door as I lay in bed. He was chatting and laughing quietly with the other nurses in the corridor. His black boots were crossed over against the door frame. As the talk quietened, I noticed his boots were increasing in size, just as the man's book at Hartlepool General had done. Eventually the boots were long and thin, maybe 1.5 feet each in length, giving Eastwood a preternatural appearance, like something out of a strange fairy-tale. I began to think he was Death, the guardian between the two worlds; that our game of pool was a variation on the usual game of chess to decide the participant's fate. I wondered whether the fact that I had lost the game meant I was now dead, and Death now about to hand me over to the ferryman who would transport me across the Styx. But I had no coins with which to pay the ferryman.

I looked up at the ceiling. The same upward-spiralling that I had noticed in the early morning was taking place, as though luring me upward. I felt as though I were about to ascend into astral flight, to leave my body behind and escape through the ceiling. As I watched, the tunnel became more elaborate, black bricks with red mortar, turning around slowly like some illusion on a fairground ghost train. Hypnotised, I watched with circumspection, as I realised I was moving up the tunnel. When I reached the end of it I realised I was in astral flight. I was moving through clouds and sky with no boundaries, no fixities or definites. I looked down at St Luke's, its orange street lamp glow, incredulous that I was free.

But it was dark, and I had lost my way. Rooftops scrolled below me, rows of houses and streetlamps. I felt no fear of falling, though suddenly my flight went into reverse, moving backwards past the same Middlesbrough residential area. A downward pull brought me to earth, back through the tunnel, black brick with red mortar ...

I opened my eyes. Eastwood was still there, his boots back to their normal size. I looked up at the ceiling, puzzled. The tunnel had gone. As I watched, however, it began to be silently reconstructed brick by brick. I looked at Eastwood and saw his boots lengthening, his sky-blue eyes bright through the darkness, gazing at me with intensity. It was time to go, the vision said. The boots were the signal that it was the right moment for us to travel. I got out of bed, picked up my clothes from the floor and put them on. I approached the threshold, Eastwood still eyeing me.

'Eastwood, I'm James Fountain. Do you need the password?'

'Hmm?' he asked. He remained still.

'Panama, Berkeley, Panama.'

'What does that mean?' he asked, his voice deep and mysterious.

'Oh, maybe it's the wrong code. How about Sherlock Holmes?'

The man rose from his chair. 'I think you'd better get back into bed, son,' he said gently. 'You see, it's not your turn to go yet. You wait, it won't be long. Get some rest, now.'

I took off my clothes and climbed back into bed. Eastwood resumed his position by the door, his feet on the door frame. Pleased to have located the first of the two men I was to meet on 3 March, I closed my eyes and felt suddenly relaxed. I slept, happy that ends were beginning to meet. I dreamt of an enormous bridge that connected heaven and earth, gradually being constructed by invisible hands.

In the morning I awoke to find Eastwood gone, and that Charlie had taken his place. I took a bath and dressed in fresh clothes – a dark-blue shirt and black jeans. Walking downstairs I felt a renewed sense of hope. All was clear to me now – I must be co-operative and patient. I took the breakfast things out of the cupboard and began laying them out on the tables as I remembered from the first day that I stepped into the building. Wilma came downstairs, wide-eyed with shock.

'Vell, James! This *is* a surprise! You've set all ze tables!' she said.

'Yes. It's a lovely day, isn't it?' I said, looking out of the window at the early morning sky, only thin streaks of white cloud marring an otherwise consistent pastel blue.

'You seem maarch better, James, I'm so pleased. I'll go and start the breakfast.'

I sat looking through the window, an elderly lady, decrepit and fragile lowering herself into a wheelchair, her small, stout husband pushing the chair stoically towards the hospital entrance. I looked up at the windows opposite and saw faces peering from windows, figures clad in pyjamas. I wondered if they could see me staring back as their eyes seemed to catch my own. I wondered if they knew what I knew.

After breakfast was over I went into the lounge, content to let Charlie do the washing up with Katie. I was in the mood for quiet and reading, so was delighted to see the day's newspaper folded up on the table. I unfolded it, and realised it was *The Sun*. I flicked casually through the pages. And then something twisted within me, made my heart miss a beat, left me desperately swallowing air as my eyes caught on to one of the headlines like suction grips.

ANTI-DRUG BOY IS LEFT A ZOMBIE BY SPIKED DRINK
Pushers target James, 16

I gazed incredulously at the headline. I stared at my photograph, which had been taken over a year before. There were braces on my teeth, my hair in that same centre-parted curtains style everyone my age seemed to have at the time. I read on, though by now my hands were shaking so much that it was difficult to keep the text in focus.

A brilliant schoolboy who stood up to drug pushers was left a 'zombie' after his lemonade was spiked at an exams party.
Police believe 16-year-old James Fountain was

96

deliberately targeted for warning fellow pupils of the risks
of getting hooked ...

I walked quickly around the room, driven by a subconscious notion that the tension could be worn off by exercise. The previous day's memories and Julian's words merged with the text as I scanned it. My eyes were so unsteady that there was no possibility of reading the entire article – my concentration was now so poor that it would not allow it. Instead my eyes seemed to select pieces of text at random – sentences, phrases – though I was so overwhelmed that I was unable to understand their true significance. The paper emitted waves of shock like radiation.

By the end of the £6-a-head party James was acting oddly
and three girls took him home.
The star cricketer – who was due to set off on a school
ski trip today ... Detective Chief Inspector Stewart, leading
the hunt for the sick pushers, said: 'It could be he will never
be the same.'

So the truth was steadily surfacing. It 'could be' that I would 'never be the same'. Life would never be the same. But the article spoke to me as a fragment of the world's response to my vision. The non-believers had yet to be convinced. According to them I had merely 'acted oddly', having unwittingly ingested a spiked drink, a poisoned chalice. The world had invented its own story to rationalise events rather than accept them for what they were.

His lawyer dad Chris and mum Barbara thought he was
drunk.

'Give us that, will you? It's my paper,' Charlie said, startling me by suddenly ripping it out of my hands, hurriedly leaving the room as he took it away. I pondered the last sentence I had read. Maybe my mother and father thought I had a drink problem. Perhaps *that* was why I was here.

I looked through the panes of glass of the patio door, eager to escape the room, which was now filling with Judith, Helen, Charlie, the boy with gelled ginger hair whose name I did not know, Katie, and the army of younger kids. I wanted to get out there and put everything straight, to set up my soapbox and address my public, to tell them what had really happened. To get on the plane and go to the mountains, to return to London to speak with the PM, to jet off to speak to the President of the United States, to talk with the UN Secretary General ... I felt great unease at the falsity of these allegations.

As I watched from the window, looking through the squares of glass that were the bars of my prison, I saw someone getting out of a car with a large camera, a cigarette tucked into the corner of his mouth, a pale overcoat and long sideburns. He hurried out of the car towards me. I waved, hoping he would come and take my photo and write the true story in his notebook.

When he was 2 metres or so from the window at which I stood, he stopped and positioned himself, aiming his paparazzi machine at my figure. Suddenly I saw three or four other cars pulling up without parking and people jumping out, cameras in hand, hurrying to take up positions. Feeling as though I was about to be shot by firing squad, I turned away from the window, closing the curtains feverishly behind me. I had merely added fuel to their fire. They wanted photos of the saint from the latest drugs crusade, not the saint who would team with the other eleven disciples to resolve the world, to usher in the Golden Age.

'What do ya think ya doin'? People want a bit of light in the room ya know!' Charlie said.

'Leave them! People are taking photos of me – it's not fair ... their stories are all wrong!' I said, desperate.

'What stories?' Charlie asked, trying to reassure me that

everything would be OK, his tone of voice gravy-like as though I were some cute Yorkshire Terrier he was greeting. He walked over and pulled back the curtains by the patio door, and suddenly flashes of lightning lit his face ghostly white in the dark February day, the room resonating with the thrilled conversations of youngsters, giggling and getting up to look at the firing squad of photographers. After the initial shock, Charlie snapped the curtains shut and spun round.

'Right, everyone leave the curtains shut, you hear? Anyone that opens them'll be in trouble!' he said loudly, looking round the room, guardian-like. Looking at the floor beneath the curtains, I saw the lightning continue for a few seconds, then stop. At this time, the local news blared out its latest bulletin on the television, which seemed to be at a high volume now that the room had retreated into a stunned silence.

'Local schoolboy James Fountain has –'

Trembling, I listened to the first words of the new headline I had expected, then Katie switched the channel. Has what? I thought to myself. '– has communicated the significances that he initially intended.' I looked around the room and saw no one looking particularly affected by hearing my name read out on the morning news, bar Katie.

'Katie, put that back on a minute, will you? You're always watching *Jerry Springer*.'

'No! The news is boring,' she insisted. She knew what the headline was going to be. But she was a non-believer.

I asked Charlie if I could go to the toilet, and he led me to it down the dirty yellow corridor. I walked in and looked in the mirror. I saw Charlie watching intently through his small blue eyes, and then my own eyes, dark little wells my sight fell down as I looked into the frightened and dilated pupils. Deep ridges lay beneath them, their greyish-black colour accentuated by the paleness of the face staring back at me. Various spots had sprouted up around the oily surface of the skin. The image heightened my anxiety.

Shaking slightly, I was about to urinate when Charlie produced a container from his trouser pocket and pushed it into my hand, asking me to urinate into it. I did as he requested, too preoccupied to ask why. When it was full I gave it back to him, my hand still shaking and spilling a little of it on his designer shoes as he cursed and screwed on the cap and I continued pissing. When I had finished I waited for Charlie as he washed his hands then feverishly scrubbed the bit of spilt urine from his shoe.

'Sorry mate.' I said.

'Ah, forget it, man. You're just a bit shook up, that's all.'

In the gloom of the lounge, dimly lit by the light from the passageway, I whiled away the afternoon watching TV. I ate nothing for lunch, and nor did anyone remind me. A certain disturbance seemed to have run around the other members of the ward, and Charlie and Wilma were busily attending to them. Even Katie seemed agitated, up and down the stairs to collect things from her room, frustrated and dismissive in her replies when I tried to make conversation. She sat at the table between us, drawing shapes on white paper, in dark colours that seemed laden with nihilism.

I was becoming conscious of a growing fear. The tomb lid seemed to have suddenly shut with the closing of the curtains, and my entrapment seemed complete. Sitting on a couch with my legs crossed and my feet shaking violently, I gazed at the closed curtains and imagined the multitude that would be gathering outside, awaiting my return. I felt certain that I would be denied the liberty of greeting the masses, that as each hour passed by I was being steadily forgotten.

I looked anxiously about the room. Judith and Helen were playing pool, Charlie was talking gently to the boy with gelled ginger hair, who was looking solemnly at the floor. I heard a telephone ringing in the office and jumped up to answer it, but was prevented by Charlie, standing suddenly and making a barrier with his arms, saying it was not for me.

But as I sat back down, I heard the conversation clearly, Dr Anderson's voice, my name mentioned several times, and the phone replaced. She had said I was still very ill, that I could not be allowed out, nor could I be allowed to address the people. The phone rang again, and a similar conversation took place. And then again.

'They're talking about me,' I said aloud to myself, a trembling finger on my lip, my eyes feeling wide in their sockets as they shifted about the room. Katie looked up from her strange designs.

'What?'

'I can hear them – here – in the office. Talking about me.'

'What are you on about? There's a soundproof door to the office. You can't hear anyone, it's your imagination.'

'You're a non-believer. If you believed me you'd know that I have special powers of hearing. I can hear through walls. They're talking about me, they want to know everything about me.'

'Oh, you're no fun anymore – you're just a weirdo.' She got up and went to talk to Charlie, who was still sitting with the ginger-haired boy. She laughed at some joke he cracked, then left the room. Charlie turned his head and looked at me, so serious that I was compelled to look the other way. I thought about the word. Weirdo.

Even when I sat down for dinner, I felt certain there were cameramen still lurking outside. Through the open curtain I saw something move in the darkness, envisaged a pale face reaching the window and raising his machine, sealing my fate. The masses would be non-believers, influenced by the media. They would see me in a hospital and draw their own conclusions.

'There's someone out there!' I shouted. 'Shut the curtains!'

'No,' Charlie said, 'There's no one out there, there never was. It's your imagination. But we might as well shut 'em now it's dark.' He closed the curtains and sat back down, shooting a smile at Katie sitting to his right.

'I saw that! You're all in this together, aren't you? Ganging up on me, trying to make me look a fool! I know what I saw, I know what's going on! You're just trying to fix me up as another ordinary person like the rest of you ratherthansome-onewhocanguideyouthrougheverything!'

'Eh? Did you understand what he just said?' Katie asked Charlie. I was being excluded just as I had expected. A new tone had developed among them. The tone of the non believers.

'No. His mind's racing so he's speakin' too fast. Look James, eat your dinner, alright? You haven't touched it.' I saw that Katie and Charlie and everyone else in the room had finished their main course. I also saw that everyone had stopped talking and was now staring at me. I looked at the tablets I was supposed to take, lying beside a glass of water.

'I won't do what you tell me from now on. I'm not taking those fucking tablets, I'm not eating this fucking food! Fuck you all!' I picked up the tablets and flung them violently across the room, smashing like pieces of chalk against the wall. There was an audible intaking of breath like the sound of a class at primary school when someone has said something naughty to the teacher.

'Now what have you done?' Charlie asked. 'You're not in a very good mood today are you? Been cranky all day.'

At that moment, Wilma hurried into the room and faced me. 'James, you are very aggressive now. I sink ve maast give you extra tablets.'

I laughed. 'I'm not taking any tablets. Like I said to Charlie here, you can all go and fuck yourselves.'

'Don't you dare use zat langvidge vis me! If you don't take ze tablets I vill have to inject ze medicine through a vein!'

The idea of an injection terrified me. I sensed I was being forced into something, being put down like a rabid dog.

'I know what those tablets are for, they're to kill me. You're going to make it look like I died naturally of something, when all the time you were slowly but surely poisoning me to death. How do I know this food you've given me's not poisoned?' I had the complete attention of the room, but for a few excited whispers. Katie and Charlie looked disgusted, Wilma flabbergasted.

'I can't believe zis, James. You ver fine zis morning when you came down for breakfast. Leave your food zen and come vis me.'

I followed her down the corridor and watched her taking out tablets from a cupboard. As she brought each container out she carefully explained what the tablet was, and what it was for, words like 'calm' and 'slow' and phrases like 'stops your mind racing' and generally making the tablets sound about as attractive as if they contained cyanide.

'I like my mind the way it is, thanks. I see you're just trying to dull my senses, to stop my powers from working. You can put those away now.'

Wilma sighed. 'Right. I'll give zem to your night nurse, and if you don't take zem ve'll have to give you an injection.' She pronounced the word 'injection' in an intensely clinical way which reminded me of the word 'execution'.

As I sat in front of the TV I listened intently to the conversations of those now walking up and down the corridor. There was surely a plot involved, people who wanted to keep me quiet. Katie came in smiling, then began frowning the moment her eyes met mine, and she loitered in the doorway until Charlie came into the room, at which point she returned to her usual smiling self. Judith and Helen sat as far away from me as possible, and the kids all raced each other to the pool table then fought over who should play the first game. There never seemed to be anything wrong with these kids. I wondered why they were not at home.

I sat, isolated and rejected, sad that life was now passing me by, that I had become part of the furniture in a house I had no wish to be in.

Meanwhile, the TV screen seemed to be projecting itself some 2 feet beyond its original frame. I remembered some tacky horror film in which the Devil hid inside a TV, yet this seemed something more. I watched the eyes of the characters of *Eastenders*, the black bags under them more pronounced, drinking their pints and vodkas in the Queen Vic. The Devil was nudging me, telling me this was the kind of freedom I would never enjoy, that my current existence will last for all eternity. That when I died I would receive the scant consolation of the title 'saint'.

When Terry came into the room I began to think of other ways in which these jailors could be trying to get to me. Perhaps Terry was with Rachel Lockwood during the day, perhaps he was holding her hostage. Perhaps he raped her. Images of this possibility flooded my mind like acid and corroded its corners. Frightened, I looked at everyone in the room, feeling like a hostage myself. I realised for the first time that I could trust no one, that I was utterly alone. And all the while Katie continued her conversation with Charlie, her laughter taunting me, echoing grotesquely around my mind like a merry-go-round.

Later, when I went into my bedroom, I looked out through the window, and tried to discern an escape route. I opened the window, which budged only an inch and let in some freezing night air. To my left was a metal drainpipe that could be used, though as I gazed into the distance I imagined there would be some form of electric fence, a gate which required a special key, and sharply spiked fencing, preventing one from vaulting over with any certainty. As I imagined these things, they seemed to come into view, my eyes focussing with superhuman efficiency. It was as I had feared – neither my parents nor anyone else could help me. Everyone had lulled me through the trap door, and now, in this prison masquerading as a hospital ward they had me where they wanted, and would exact upon me whatever torture they pleased. I expected nothing less than for Wilma and her co-conspirators to offer up excruciating injections, followed eventually by my execution.

'Right, son, get into bed,' came a voice, 'tha's nothin' ta see out there.' The Wilbur Smith man had returned. No more Eastwood. Of course. He would have been taken captive too. The man's pitiless gaze shifted from me to the bed, and I did as he said.

But as I lay there in the darkness I became increasingly anxious. What had initially been a kind of vision of my imminent torture and destruction at the hands of the non-believers now became a vivid and terrifying realisation. I no longer viewed the potentials from afar. I now saw them close up, at the forefront of my consciousness. I watched my future scroll out upon the wall in front of me. It was all very plain what the pattern was. I was fine, while they called me sick. I had not slept as I could not be certain where I was or why I was here. It was time to move on, as evidently those who were to assist in my escape had been captured, and no doubt butchered.

Jumping out of bed in an intense flurry of activity, I pulled the empty suitcase from under my bed and ripped my clothes from the wardrobe. I shoved them into the suitcase, plus my toothbrush, hairbrush and anything else I could find. I wore my strong Doc Marten shoes with steel toe caps, and brightly coloured clothes – white jeans and red T-shirt, so as to catch the attention of any passing cars on my escape to the road, to hitch a lift back home. I could plan things better when I got there, talk things over with my mother and father.

I was ready. I picked up the suitcase and turned toward the door, suddenly conscious of the presence of the man with lifeless eyes.

'Where do you think you're going?' he asked, his voice deeper and more aggressive than before.

'I'm leaving, you can't keep me here. You bastards are going to pay for this!'

'Now that's enough, son.' His voice had slipped into the kind of calming tone I'd heard used in movies where someone would try to talk someone out of suicide, down from a skyscraper or cliff edge. 'Let's put down the bag. That's it. Now, take off your clothes, and get into bed.'

As he looked over his shoulder briefly I saw my opportunity, and took the bag and ran past him to the fire exit. My heart thumped furiously and my breath was gone as I guessed at four-digit security codes and punched them into the plastic key pad. Each time I failed there was a loud electronic blare, and I swore and punched the wall and tried again. I knew it began with '35', having noticed this over Terry's shoulder on our way through the door one night. But with each attempt came the agonising blare hammering my ear drums, blood gushing around my body ever faster as my heart pounded the riotous music of hell in double time.

Now I heard footsteps behind me, another slow drum beat against the thinly carpeted floor, coming closer. I smashed my right shoe into the glass, but my toe cap came up against the wire mesh, which would not budge. By now the man had his hands on my shoulders and I disappeared down the corridor to escape him, the air wheezing in my ears as I ran with fear and panic-fuelled speed to the door at the other end. I kicked it as hard as I could with my heavy shoes but realised it was not going to budge, and continued to kick at it and swear in pent-up frustration. In seconds I was grabbed, my arms forced behind my back, and led back down the corridor by my keeper, Katie and all the rest of the in-patients standing in sleepy disturbance, their alarmed faces peering beyond doorways. There was no way out.

11

I stared dumbly at my bacon and egg, then ate. The food seemed to taste alright, but they were sure to have developed a special poison that was tasteless. But after another sleepless night, lying there watching my thoughts compile fears of eternal entrapment, watching the darkness fade to bring in another hopeless day, my stomach was as empty as the hope that surrounded me.

I left half of my food for the rest of the world. At least I could do some good in my own small way, even if I was being somewhat restricted.

'Eat it up, son,' came Tim's monotonous predictable words. I ignored him and looked at the half-finished plate, resolved. I could hear Katie speeding up her eating. She had not talked to me so far and I could tell she wanted to get away from the table as quickly as possible. 'No clever games, now. Eat it up.' Tim kept this up for a few more minutes and then gave up. I looked stubbornly at the half-empty plate. Then I had an idea and put the tablets in my glass of water.

'Eh! What yer doin', man!' I watched the tablets dissolve quickly and without trace into the water. Maybe all the drinking water contained dissolved pills. 'You do realise you've gotta drink that now, don't you?'

'No, he doesn't, Tim. It'll make him sick zat vay. You should know zat. I'll get him some more.'

'Don't you talk to me like that *Wil*-ma!' said Tim, becoming increasingly irate. This was a new development, arguments amongst the conspirators. Clearly I was breaking them down.

'Take it easy, Tim!' I said, mockingly. 'You'll feel better soon, lad. Take your tablets.' The room burst into laughter.

Tim boiled with rage, his eyes looming large and bloodshot in their sockets.

'Shut up, you!' he stammered.

'Oooh, temper, temper!' I said, twisting the knife. Now even Katie was laughing as Tim's face contorted with rage.

When Wilma returned I took the tablets and drank them down. My new elated mood allowed nothing to get in its way, and all of the anger and paranoia seemed to have suddenly evaporated.

Later, I ate a decent lunch of soup and sandwiches prepared with the help of Katie, and we laughed and joked as we ate, having happily resumed our friendship. Making fun of Tim had brought us closer together.

As we sat rebelliously eating our lunch in the lounge watching dull Sunday offerings on the television, the doorbell rang. Katie jumped up to see who it was, as she was expecting friends. But I heard her talking with people whose voices were vaguely familiar. She walked back in and announced that my father and sister had come to visit.

I was overcome with joy. I jumped up and shook my father's hand, who smiled, though my sister looked rather concerned, surveying the room with her large brown eyes, her hair tied in a single schoolgirlish plait. My father looked tired, his eyes bloodshot at the edges. The irises reminded me of little blue marbles I once owned.

'So, you're doing okay, then?' he asked. That's what he wanted to hear, that I was okay. To skirt around the danger and hope it would go away.

'Yes, I'm fine!' I said, not wanting to burden him with recent traumas, though I was now thoroughly unburdened. 'They won't let me out though, they don't understand the work I've got to do.'

'Well, you can worry about your GCSEs later, can't you? You'll soon be out,' he said breezily, as if I had just had my tonsils taken out and was waiting to be discharged at some point later in the day.

'No, I mean my work to help save humanity, as St James,' I explained. My sister's face screwed up into a scowl.

'*What?*' she more stated than asked. 'Can't you just start making some sense just for five minutes?'

'Quiet, Victoria!' my father snapped. She sulked slightly, as if this were some ordinary fraternal dispute at home. I had already ascertained that my sister was a disbeliever at our last meeting. My father's features brightened as he spotted the pool table. 'Do you want a game of pool, James? Victoria and I against you?'

I set up the balls, and my father broke, marvelling at the quality of the pool cues: 'Just the right weight.' As I launched into an explanation of what they were and the power they contained my father scratched his head and said, 'Oh, right,' in the way he always did when he was feigning interest. But I felt he could be worked on, he was not a lost cause like Victoria.

We played several games, and I could tell my father was helping me to win. Yet for all his treating me like a child, I was glad of the kindness. I watched his easy, relaxed movements and gently smiling face with admiration. He was such a contrast to the gruff men at work on the ward. I looked across at Tim lying back on a sofa. In between shots, I explained to my father that I didn't like Tim's particular brand of care, to which he replied that he had thought Tim was one of the patients. Katie overheard my father's comment and laughed hilariously.

'Who's *she?*' Victoria asked quietly, scanning the room. 'You've got some right weirdos in 'ere haven't you?'

I didn't even bother to reply. She had never liked the girls I was friends with. Always called them 'weird'. She stared in particular at Judith and her gothic eye make-up, who returned the stare. And I saw her looking with sympathy at Annette, who I was glad was reading and didn't notice.

I played table tennis with my dad while my sister mooched

around, running a finger over the books in the bookcase until it filled with dust, clearing her throat with disgust. I saw her looking through the patio window as I had done many times, moving down to the fish tank to look at the fish, no doubt trying to imagine herself in my shoes. I watched my father keeping up his end, both of us poor at table tennis but managing to keep our rallies going up to about 20, himself having not played for 'years' as he put it.

Katie's friends arrived, both of them young men who I guessed were slightly older than her, in their early twenties, dressed in flares and sixties-style shirts and denim jackets. They appeared briefly in the lounge while Katie pointed me out and muttered a few words, then laughed and disappeared down the corridor towards the kitchen.

'Reminds me of the clothes I wore when I was a student!' my father commented.

And soon the game of table tennis was over and my father put down his bat and said, 'right, we'd better go, James,' and peeled my sister away from the TV, who was now lying sloppily across a couch with her shoes off as she did when she was at home. How I missed home.

And now they were leaving, a last handshake from my father, a light hug from my sister and a final wave of hands and a 'we'll see you soon' and then I heard the door bang shut and they were gone.

I ran around the pool table 12 times, and then around the table tennis table 12 times. Something had to be done, someone had to help. A storm of mixed emotions raged in my mind as I remembered home and my mother and my father and my sister and myself at some point content. That now seemed long ago, and everything had been taken away save the freedom I felt in enacting these controls. At least I knew this system worked, that it would remind God to set the wheels of change in motion, to put mine and everyone else's world to rights.

As I completed my final lap of the table tennis table, I saw a man who I'd never seen before walking towards me, in his mid-thirties with blond hair parted in the middle, wearing a pair of circular blue spectacles whose lenses magnified his remarkable hazel eyes. I stopped running and shook his open hand. He told me his name was Dr Randall, a consultant psychiatrist working under Dr Anderson, and asked me to follow him to the office.

Dr Randall was tall, his chair seeming too low for him as we sat either side of the desk. His voice was commanding as he began his inquisition.

'So! How do you feel?'

'Like I want to go home.' I considered, and decided I could trust him. He had a solid countenance. 'I'm frightened of this place.'

'Frightened.' He wrote the word in his notes. 'Why?' His magnified eyes blinked at me as he rested his folded arms on the desk.

'The people in charge here don't like me. They want me dead.' My mind fogged over. Just saying the words tinged my every thought with gloom.

'You do look rather agitated,' the doctor said, peering over the table for an instant at my shaking feet, 'rather hyperactive. Are you sure you're taking all of your pills?'

'I don't like pills. Especially *their* pills. They're laced with poison, they're trying to spike my food ...' I stood up. 'I want to go home. Can I use the phone, please?'

'No!' Dr Randall barked, raising a commanding voice, 'Sit down! Good. Now, I can't stress this enough, if you don't take your pills, you will not get well, which means you will not go home.'

'But I *am* well!' I protested.

'That's not true. Your E.E.G. is abnormal. Your cognition, according to Dr Anderson's records, is not as it should be. Last time you saw her you even replied incorrectly when she

111

asked you what year we are in. You are not sleeping well, you are not eating well, you are paranoid ...'

'*You* would be if you knew what was going on in here! None of you have any idea, neither you nor Dr Anderson. When you leave, everythingchangesandI'mnolongersafe!' The words tumbled out clumsily and angrily. I felt my speech speeding up and I knew he would neither believe nor understand me. I had missed a cruicial opportunity to explain myself and the danger I faced. As it was, he just kept on talking, listing my deficiencies:

'... your mind is racing, you have severe mood swings ...'

'As does any great person! Look, will you just listen to me? Iknowwhatsreallygoingonhere!' There was a pause. My shouting rang in my ears for a few seconds, and then receded. I heard the wind whistling to itself beyond the window.

'I know this is difficult for you. But you must – slow – down. Now, can you count backwards for me in threes from a hundred?'

A test. Maybe it would lead to freedom if I passed, to feeling the wind on my face ...

'One hundred, ninety-seven ... ninety-four ...' This was tough. Amid the foggy atmosphere I attempted to sight the numbers, and slowly they came into view, though sometimes a number would vanish and it would seem like hours before I could come up with the next one. Dr Randall was jotting down notes. Finally I reached the number one.

'Well, you got there in the end. I make that eleven minutes,' he said, looking at his watch, 'and I think for an intelligent young man like you, that was pretty slow. Be honest with me, your concentration's poor, isn't it?'

'Yes,' I admitted. I had never realised exactly how poor until that moment.

'Well, we'll sort that out. I'm prescribing an extra tablet that might do the trick. Make sure you take it.'

'But I'm tired. I need rest, not pills.' The doctor glanced at

112

me and smiled, his hazel eyes catching the light.

'I'm the doctor here. Your mind needs to be slowed down.'

I felt the fuse being lit, the fog clearing, the anger burning. 'Exactly. So you're one of them, trying to take away my special powers. Just because you're not special!'

'You're being inappropriate and aggressive. Wilma!' he shouted. I stood.

'So what's your game exactly, eh? You think you can shut me up, lock me away so that you non-believers can prevent the Golden Age from beginning! EH!' The door burst open and Wilma and Tim came bustling into the room. Tim grabbed my hands from the desk and forced them behind my back.

'Just FUCK OFF!' I shouted, Wilma opening her quivering hand to reveal yet more tablets. No more, I thought. I wasn't about to let them keep me silent.

I struggled desperately and wrenched an arm free, jabbing Tim in his belly with an elbow, and sped down the corridor, past the lounge, the kitchen and the dining room. I hid in one of the toilet cubicles, gasping for breath, drinking in the oxygen that they were trying to snuff out. Everything Randall said was a lie. Dr Anderson had been knocked off or pensioned off, and now they had some false doctor who would keep up a respectable front, whilst marshalling a terrorist attack. The Devil was striking back.

'James! Open ze door or ve vill break it down!'

'Go away! I know what you're up to Vil-maa! Bugger off!'

'Don't use zat langvidge, please!' She lowered her voice to a whisper, 'Tim get ze screwdriver.' I decided to give up. There was no possible way out. I opened the door. Wilma put her hand on her heart. Evidently she had been afraid I would commit suicide, that my death would come too early. That it would be by my own hand and not hers.

'I'm not taking those tablets.'

They each took one of my arms and led me slowly down the corridor to the small room, linked by a window to the back of the office.

'Zis is ze observation room. You vill stay in here until you take those pills.' And then Wilma left me, locking the door, Tim sitting on the single bed. Wilma appeared in the office, she and Dr Randall debating with wide gesticulations, exasperated expressions across their faces. I was tougher than they had expected. I smiled and looked out at the exit gate from the small window.

'You'll never get home you know,' Tim said, 'because you're thick. You won't take your pills. You won't eat your food.' I sat on the chair by the window, avoiding his cruel eyes.

'Shut the fuck up,' I said.

'DON'T YER DARE TALK TO ME LIKE THAT!' he shouted. Suddenly Wilma was running through from the office and unlocking the door.

'Tim! Keep it down! You maast be kinder to him.' She was right. Or else I might do what I'd been thinking about, break the window, get some glass. Find an artery.

After Wilma left and locked the door once more, I paced about the room for some time, petrified. Moving the chair further away from Tim, whose leaden, bloodshot eyes kept a constant watch upon me from his slouched position on the bed, I sat and contemplated a swift exit. I could end it all right now. There was no need for any of this to continue. I would try not to breathe, as the REM song went. I could hold my breath and cease. It would be my own doing, my reaction against oppression. I seized upon this moment of clarity, and took in a deep long breath, closed my eyes, and held it.

I counted seconds in my mind. I began to see the tunnel extending up beyond the ceiling, but this time the bricks were white, and the mortar sky-blue. I was travelling up it, towards salvation. A cloud city came into view, far away at the end of the white tunnel. I heard a voice, faint and distant, exasperated.

'James! James! Come on son, talk to me! James! Don't do

this to yerself!' I turned briefly in mid-air and saw the little room in my mind, myself sitting there, locked inside it. I saw Tim's lips moving, his hands on top of his head. I saw my face, eyes closed, head fallen forward on to my chest. My lungs ached. The numbers were in the two hundreds now, floating down the tunnel as little cloud formations: 210, 211, 212 ...

213. Suddenly the image automatically rewound itself and I came back through the tunnel and opened my eyes, aware of hands on my shoulders, gasping for air, coughing and spluttering. Seeing Tim standing over me through my tear-blurred vision. My heart pumping furiously, sickened at my attempt to stop it, hyperactive upon the realisation that I had failed. But now at least I knew it was possible. All that would be required in order to succeed was practice. Words that I had expected became audible through the pounding of blood, as if I'd done this all before.

'Now that was silly, wasn't it? Yer could've killed yerself!' I listened wearily to the words of the world I wanted to escape. The psychobabble of reason. Trapped in a small room, refusing to take tablets, cut off from humanity, persecuted as a saint they thought was a madman. I felt I had every right to be wanting to leave, one way or another.

I refused to take the pills Tim offered, becoming more and more convinced they contained cyanide or some other poison, that this room was the place designated for my removal from a world that could no longer contain me, an execution chamber. I gazed at the locked door, and drew in another breath. Through half-open eyes I saw Wilma and Dr Randall close by the window, looking anxiously in. I closed my eyes and felt the pain in my lungs, my heart stopping ... but it was too much. My eyes shot open and filled with water, and I looked above and prayed for help to end the nightmare. Tim's cold gaze frightened and bemused me, and I wondered how anyone could be so cruel. He smiled and offered up the tablets once more.

I could see Dr Randall preparing a syringe. The lethal injection. An idea came to me and I took the pills from Tim's open hand and put them in my mouth, waited until he looked away towards the window, then carefully removed them and threw them on to the carpet behind me. The vile taste of the partially dissolved pills had settled on my tongue as an extra layer.

'Eh, yer 'aven't taken them!' came Tim's voice. His wild black hair and frustrated eyes reminded me of a fat Heathcliffe, frightening as he fixed upon the area of carpet behind my chair.

Suddenly Wilma came bustling back in with the syringe and more tablets and offered me a straight choice.

'You choose, James. It's von or ze other.'

Realising I now had no choice, I took the tablets and swallowed them, this time using the water offered to rid my mouth of the disgusting aftertaste. I hoped death would come quickly. God would send me back in some other form to complete my work.

But nothing changed. I remained in the same chair facing the door for the rest of the afternoon, until darkness fell behind me. So it was to be a slow death. I watched the door intently and envisaged my escape the next time it opened. I could get my stomach pumped at Accident and Emergency, I could be on my way the very next day. All was not lost.

I felt my mind slowing down, so much so that by the time the door opened I was not on the edge of my seat ready for action, but asleep. I awoke to see the door open and Wilma shaking me, my limbs heavy. The poison was taking effect, but I no longer cared. I anticipated death as a person standing at a bus stop waiting for the number 9 into town.

Wilma helped me to my feet and supported me down the corridor to the dining-room, my vision blurred and my eyelids barely half open. I staggered along. Katie came out of the lounge and looked at me as I walked past, I smiled back drunkenly, as a flicker of disturbance passed across her face.

116

When Wilma put me into my usual chair, my head fell against the table, and I felt the energy leaking out of my body like petrol from a rusty old engine. My time had come, and I felt content. I became aware of voices above me murmuring, which came to me like the sporadic moments during an operation when the patient thinks he hears the voices of surgical staff chatting amongst themselves.

I smelt food and managed to open my eyes a quarter. I touched them in surprise, unable to believe that this was it, that total lock down had been initiated. It was happening. I felt jabs to my thin right bicep. Instinctively I lifted up my head, heavy as a paving stone, and looked at Tim, my mouth hanging open uncontrollably.

I ate what tasted like sausage and chips carefully, slowly, as Annette did. It was all involuntary, slowed by the poison, dying like a whale moored upon a beach.

'I shot the albatross,' I said aloud, looking half-consciously at my food.

'Eh?' said the voice to my right. Coleridge's words came back to me through a slight clearing in the drowsy haze.

'Alone, alone, all, all alone,
Alone on a wide, wide sea!
And never a saint took pity on
My soul in agony.'

'Well, that's clever!' came the voice, 'It even rhymes!' I pushed away my half-finished plate and my head slumped on to the table.

'It's Co-le-ridge,' I said drowsily, 'you've shot me. I'm the albatross.'

When I came to Katie was shaking me, and the room was empty. Tim, Wilma and some of the night nurses hovered in the corridor.

'James ... James, are you alright?' she asked gently. Terry

approached and motioned for her to go down to the lounge.

'OK. Let's get you up the stairs.'

He eventually managed to get me up the staircase, though I lost my footing several times on the polished wooden steps. Again I tried to see the code he typed but could not keep my eyes focussed or open for long enough. Once through the door, I was taken to my room where I was helped out of my clothes, before falling onto the bed into a deep hole of unconsciousness.

When I next opened my eyes it was morning, and I was struck by the possibility that I must now be dead, and therefore a ghost. Maybe everyone here was a ghost and this had happened to all the rest of the patients already. That would be how the staff prevented everyone from getting home – because no one else could see them.

But I could see my face in the small mirror beside my bed, realising I was alive, and nothing resolved. I put on my glasses and saw a tired, wasted reflection, my eyes crestfallen and broken. The drowsy sensation remained. I stood and heard people talking in the corridor, the splash of water as people bathed and brushed their teeth like soldiers in barracks, the nurses getting them up into their regular drill so that they made it down to breakfast on time.

The early morning sky resembled the mottled grey of an old tombstone. It could promise me nothing but death.

12

Four days passed in a similar vein. Sleep was a rarity at this time, though exhaustion took its toll, so that finally I passed out at the end of this period as I had done on the night which preceded it.

The days stretched out ahead like long, dark tunnels. I felt a great unease and apprehension as I watched each new day dawning, my interest in life dwindling ever further. At these points I would try to suffocate myself, to send the oxygen back where it came from. And then I would fail and collapse on my bed or the floor, my lungs burning, a nurse running over, telling me I was foolish in a voice that was somehow calming and authoritative in the same instant.

The periods between breakfast and lunch, lunch and dinner, dinner and bedtime were all spent encamped in the lounge. Tim, Charlie and Wilma sat all about me, watching every movement that I made with minute interest. I sat patiently through it all, feeling defiant in the face of all this evil, these people who had taken my life away from me.

Katie headed back to her home in Redcar, and before leaving wrote down the date of a joint 20th birthday party herself and a friend were having in mid-March, assuming I was out by then, along with her address and telephone number.

'You'll be right by then, James. Don't you worry,' she said, placing a hand on my shoulder. I felt myself beginning to cry.

'I hope so. They want to keep me here, don't they?'

'No. You keep trying, alright? You'll get there in the end. It's not your fault.' And then she kissed me on the forehead, opened the front door, and was gone.

I thought about how that must feel – to be free, to feel the cold winter wind, to be getting on a bus and heading home. I imagined Katie walking proudly through the Middlesbrough streets, her backpack strapped on, the wind in her short blonde hair, looking forward to going back to art college. I looked at my captors and thought about how distant a possibility this was for myself.

By Friday I felt a little more optimistic, having had a decent night's sleep. As I ate my overcooked bacon and egg and looked at the empty space opposite where Katie had sat, I reflected upon a CT scan that had gone horribly wrong three days before. I had panicked and struggled so that the scan could not be conducted, only afterwards learning it was merely a routine brain scan. I winced at the possibility this might have set back a potential release date.

Later I saw Dr Anderson once more. I watched her turning her pen in her fingertips and eyeing my details.

'Dr Randall says you've been quite excitable over the last few days,' she said, only looking up when she had completed the sentence.

'I suppose so,' I said glumly.

'Can you tell me why?'

'I don't like it here, I want to go home.'

'You seem much better today. Did you sleep well?'

'Actually, yes. I've given up trying to fight you all. I'll do whatever I have to until you let me out.'

'That's good. I'm glad to see you've come to your senses. And if we really wanted to kill you we'd have done it by now, don't you think?'

I didn't know what to think. I just hoped Katie was right, that they were going to let me go home soon. But then maybe she was being over-optimistic.

The doctor tested my cognition, commenting it was much improved, but adding that my concentration was still poor. And then I was walking back through the door and back into the lounge and picking up a pool cue to avoid having to sit with Wilma, Tim and Charlie. I struck the pool balls powerfully about the table to relieve the ever-present tension.

Everyone had gone. Parents had been and collected their children, hugging them and lifting them up in the air. Judith and Helen had been collected by a woman who was evidently Judith's mother, with the same long, black hair but without the eyeshadow. She did wear a black suit, however. Annette had been allowed some time home.

And so here I was. Singled out. We had reached the endgame, and it was just a matter of waiting in this lounge until I cracked and they would have an excuse to put me down for good. No more tranquillizer tablets. A single bullet was all that was required to rid the world of the Man Who Knew Too Much, the visionary who held the key to the successful removal of evil from the world. They had decided it was worth releasing the more minor visionaries, so as to deal with this major one.

As I sat down on a couch between Wilma and Charlie, I felt I had the upper hand. Evidently these people were just mercenaries, hired help. Their terrorist organisation had not received the visionary material that I had. They had released some story to the press as an excuse to keep me here, they had conned my parents. But they didn't fool me. I watched Tim with half-closed eyes, staring angrily back with his red face. That would be why he drank – because he sensed this operation would end in his own imprisonment. He knew I was more powerful than his whole organisation put together.

The nurses came and went with their mugs of tea, and I declined each time they gingerly offered me one. The blue morning sky was now patched with dark grey as rain clouds began to huddle together like rugby forwards about to scrum down. Nature sensed the endgame, and reflected it.

'James, you can't keep this up forever. You know you've got to talk to us eventually. You've hardly spoken the past couple o' days.'

But I was not to be budged. I wanted them to squirm in

uncomfortable silence, for them to know who was boss. I
would win this game of mental chess. That way when they shot
me I would be remembered, and my spirit feared. I would
come back to haunt them.

The doorbell rang. The doorbell never rang. People usually
bashed on the door with their knuckles. Tim looked irritated
and started issuing orders.

'Right, I'll go. You two stay 'ere and watch 'im.'

He got up from the couch. I listened with great anticipation.
This was evidently a visit they weren't expecting. Could it be
Westmoreland? I remembered the letter at Hartlepool General
– was it 3 March already? Had my powers moved the world
forwards in time?

I heard my mother's voice and the sound of her ruffling her
coat in the hallway. I hadn't noticed it was raining. She came
bustling in, a rediscovered energy lighting up her eyes and
quickening her footsteps.

'Hi, James, you all ready to go?'

I felt myself smiling uncontrollably, unable to speak as joy
rushed around inside me, transforming the swelling urge to die
with a feverish awareness of the preciousness of life. Wilma
and Charlie rose.

'We didn't know anything about this. Who did yer speak
to?' Tim asked, his face redder, angrier. My mother looked
aghast.

'Well, I spoke to Dr Anderson about it yesterday afternoon.
It was all arranged.'

'I'll just telephone to check, Mrs Fountain. You see ve haf
had no instructions regarding zis,' Wilma stated, the staccato
rhythm in her voice unusually pronounced. Her plans had been
waylaid, interfered with by the outside world. By an interfering
mother.

Meanwhile my father had drifted into the room from his
hiding place in the hall. He liked to let my mother do the
talking. He stood quietly in his red Clipper jacket, his hands

clasped behind his back, his eyes watching his shoes as he shifted them occasionally.

'Now, Mrs Fountain,' said Wilma as she came back into the room, 'I've had a vord vis Dr Anderson and she sayz zat everysing is fine. He's maach improved today.'

'Yes, he seems much better . . . Well, let's get going!'

I sprang up and went out of the doorway, all worries and restraints lifted from me, feeling like a hostage newly released after weeks of hopeless captivity. As I followed my mother and father into the hall, having forgotten the presences of Tim and Charlie and their potential threat to my release, I met my sister who was carrying my suitcase down the hall.

'Hi, Victoria!' I exclaimed and took the suitcase from her, 'It's nice to see you again.'

As I said these words I realised I still felt a sharp unease, and as the front door opened I was certain something was about to happen, that the gun would be brought from the office, or some lethal injection quickly stabbed into my back. Surely they were not going to let me simply walk away like this, after all their hard work? Or perhaps they had decided to wait, to catch me in a few weeks when it had all died down. Or maybe in a few *years*, when my guard was down, when I had forgotten them and the threat they posed. I felt the cold air on my face, the freshness of it, entering my nostrils and luxuriating in my lungs, beginning to expel the stuffiness of the ward from my memory. I turned and looked at them all standing in the doorway with blank eyes, defeated, reluctantly waving hands, keeping up the pretence of innocence in the face of their anger.

Victoria and my parents led me to our dark-blue Volvo, the rain driving down ever harder. My father opened the boot to put my suitcase in it. I jumped at the sound of a car horn behind me, and turning I saw the sound had come from my Uncle Graham's silver Vauxhall. My mother told me to get in his car and I did so, hurrying to get out of the rain.

Getting into the back seat and closing the door I saw my

little cousin Richard, who was approaching his fourth birthday. He smiled, displaying a top row of perfect white teeth, and continued sucking at the carton of orange juice his mother had given him to keep him quiet.

'E-llo, James!' He giggled, his big blue eyes sparkling.

'Now then, James, how's it going?' asked my uncle. 'Have they been treatin' you alright?'

'Not really. You're just in time – I think they were about to do something horrible to me.'

'Well – it's over now,' he said, somewhat puzzled and indifferent.

'Yes, we're taking you to a nice place in Newcastle now,' chimed in my Aunty Beryl.

'Really? Great!'

I looked at the rain droplets hitting the window and sneaking downwards, merging together and picking up pace against their background of grey. I wondered what place this might be, a true centre for excellence perhaps. Maybe I had been diverted from my Divine training and was about to go to the place I should have been sent originally. Maybe it was ordained that Newcastle be the principal city of Westmoreland. New castle.

The rain had become heavy so that my uncle was struggling to keep my father's car in his sights. I watched as droplets hammered off the road in fury. Perhaps God was angry at the way I had been treated and this was his outpouring of grief. Through the vague mist that was accompanying the storm I could see the Elwick turn-off and thought of the people that would be drinking away as usual in The McOrville: John Southport with his pints of Guinness and quick-fire scouse humour, Ruud with his straggly blond hair and fake designer labels and smoke rings, Jack Turner and his dry, wonderfully filthy turn of phrase that delighted the work-weary tea time crowd. I wondered whether they missed me at all, whether my father had mentioned anything about me. I wondered whether my father really knew what had happened, how he would explain it.

I played with Richard and his toys and watched his clear blue eyes and happily waving arms. I understood his needs better now, and he seemed more delighted than usual with the way I played with him. Where had this knowledge come from? Maybe I had learnt something at St Luke's after all, through a kind of subliminal form of teaching. Richard laughed and giggled until he was ready to sleep, and soon I closed my own eyes and felt a welcome sense of peace engulf me.

When I awoke, dusk had fallen and we were turning left at a roundabout into Jesmond, the sign from the roundabout clearly visible now that the rain had slowed. Still the sense of peace continued, even as my uncle turned the car into Newcastle Nuffield Hospital, with its light-blue sign. We moved into the car-park, then carefully round to the back of the hospital along a narrow road with sharp corners. Richard woke with a shriek and his mother turned around to quiet him gently, her smooth voice all that was required to calm him.

I followed my uncle out of the car, and saw my father's Volvo parked immediately in front, both cars in spaces next to a side door.

'Well, James, I think you'll like it here,' said my mother, getting out of the car, 'it's very posh!'

My father took out my suitcase and closed the boot, and my sister, father, uncle, mother and myself all went through the door, my aunt staying in the car to look after Richard. A silver elevator shone to our right, and bright flowery wallpaper and a cheery pink carpet reminded me of a hotel reception. A sweet fragrance filled the air and there was a crystal vase of fresh roses on a small table beside some newspapers and a couple of chairs. My mother gave me a look accompanied by a half-smile, which I knew translated as: 'I hope you'll like this,' and called for the elevator. I watched the orange glow around the button she touched.

When the elevator door finally opened we all got in and my mother pressed button number two. Excitement pulsed through me as the elevator hummed upwards and I tried to imagine what I was about to see.

The door opened and I walked out on to a dark-blue carpet, noticing the same flowery wallpaper on the wall immediately opposite as on the ground floor. There was an office to my left where a plump lady in a dark-blue suit and large glasses sat at a computer, turning her head and smiling warmly as I looked in on her. Turning right another office lay behind a wall of glass, in front of which was a circular mahogany table with an intricately patterned ceramic vase of fake carnations, and two comfortable-looking chairs. A long corridor ran through the ward with various rooms connecting from it, leading to a living-room with a large TV set.

An attractive young woman wearing a sky-blue nurse's uniform approached from the glass-fronted office, her dark-brown hair in a ponytail. I guessed she must be 6 feet tall, a deep tan and clear brown eyes giving her a Spanish appearance.

'Hello!' she exclaimed walking enthusiastically towards me. 'You must be James! I'm Sheila. And hello, Barbara. How's the journey been?'

The tone she used with my mother was more sympathetic than enthusiastic. I watched her as my mother spoke of rain and Newcastle traffic. I was unsure about her sincerity, despite the lavishness of the decor around me, and was uncertain why this should be. But as I watched more closely she seemed very nice, her facial expression relaxed and friendly. And she was quite beautiful.

As my mother talked on and Sheila tried to stay patient I noticed other people moving around at the far end of the corridor, casually dressed like myself, going into rooms to get newspapers, lighting cigarettes that I could already smell coming from the TV room. They were all adults, and seemed to be walking very slowly.

Sheila showed me to the bedroom nearest the office with the glass front. It was bright, with a large window looking onto a neighbouring house, a hospital bed, a bedside table, a large armchair and a TV. Sheila showed me how to get Sky News, Sky Sports and other satellite channels. She also indicated a telephone beside my bed, but explained that it would be expensive to dial out.

'And look at this!' my mother exclaimed.

I turned to see her switching on a light to reveal a newly built *en suite* bathroom, with a large mirror, washbasin and toilet, but no bath or shower.

'The bathroom and shower cubicles are further down the hall. I'll show you all of that later, James. Just give us a shout and we'll be glad to assist you with anything that you require,' Sheila said, her well-spoken accent and smooth delivery more in keeping with the voice of an air hostess than that of a nurse.

'It's lovely. Thanks for bringing me here,' I said to my mother. I felt very lucky to have been rescued from St Luke's and the terrible plot that was gathering. They would catch up with me eventually, but at least my fate could be delayed. This was to be my place of rehabilitation after the ordeal I had endured. My mother hugged me tightly. As everyone moved out of the bathroom I was left alone, and I tried not to look at my reflection as I pulled the cord above the mirror to switch off the light.

My feeling of comfort had induced a drowsiness, so I took off my shoes and lay heavily on the bed. My mother sat and put a hand on my forehead, stroked the side of my face.

'Your dinner's on its way James. Then you'll be able to have a sleep. Oh, and by the way, I'll be staying here tonight – I'll be sleeping in the room next door. I just want to make sure you're happy before I go home.'

'Sure,' I replied. But I was not sure about the strange ring of permanence to her pronunciation of the words, 'before *I* go home'.

Sheila came back with a stethoscope and thermometer, and told me she needed to check my heart rate and temperature for the hospital records. After she had done so a man dressed in a white uniform entered and took some blood from a vein in my left arm. I lay on the bed the whole time, quite relaxed. My sister was unpacking my suitcase, no doubt under orders from my mother, and I heard my father and uncle talking in low voices somewhere in the corridor. My mother was elsewhere, probably talking to Sheila.

I was amazed when my meal arrived on a tray, carried by a lovely girl dressed in a traditional black and white waitress's uniform. She had short brown hair and generous-looking lips lightly coated in red lipstick. Not more than 18 or 19, I marvelled at her luminescent skin and bright blue eyes as she smiled at me and placed my food on the table. There was soup to start, with fish, potatoes and vegetables for my main course, which came in an appetizing sauce.

'Thanks very much!' I exclaimed, 'It's very kind of you to bring that in for me.'

'Oh, it's part of the service here. You always get your food in your room. Normally there's a menu too, but your mum ordered for you earlier. If you're still hungry after you can have a dessert.' She was as well-spoken as Sheila, but a little more nervous and softly spoken.

'Thanks. And what's your name?'

'Rebecca ... or just Becca. That's what my friends call me!' She smiled, slightly more at ease now the ice was broken. 'Just give me a shout if you need anything.' I watched her walk out of the room, took the lid off the ornate white soup bowl and took a sip of the greenish, wondrous-smelling leek soup. I wondered what things might have been like had I met her some other time, in some other place.

13

Shortly after I had finished my evening meal I took off my clothes and got into the crisp covers of the bed. My mother came in to tell me that everyone else had gone home, and hugged me once more and turned off the light. I watched her disappear into the room next door, and a short lady with bobbed grey hair and large circular spectacles placed a chair in my doorway and sat down. She wore the same blue uniform as Sheila, and began to read her paperback as I drifted into an exhausted sleep.

Next day I awoke and opened the curtains to find the sun beaming down on me. I watched the sun melting between the leafless skeletons of trees in the distance. From the window I could see an extensive garden visible behind the house opposite. A metal swing fluttered in the breeze, the grass long and neglected, thick with leaves. I remembered our garden swing at home and how my sister used to glide to and fro upon it, singing Christmas carols long after each New Year. Two magpies patrolled sections of the shabby lawn, inspecting their territory, and raking the leaves with their beaks.

I stretched weary limbs and touched my face, finding it lightly coated with adolescent stubble, the skin tightly drawn across the cheek bones and jaw, the randomly placed mounds of acne. I touched the large indentations that had formed beneath the eye sockets, and for a moment I stood entranced by the sudden remembrance of recent sleepless nights. I went into the bathroom and washed, scrubbing with the soap in an effort to relieve my skin of its many blemishes. I dried myself with the soft white towel provided, 'Nuffield' woven into its fabric.

Deciding to delay a visit to my mother in the next room, I

walked down the corridor to investigate my new surroundings. I looked to the right and saw the office door closed, and saw the other office also empty. I heard voices coming from the next room up on the left hand side, the door only slightly ajar, though it appeared to be a regular room like my own. I paused in front of it. The voices ceased, and then a sudden burst of laughter shocked me into continuing my ramble. On my right was a kitchen in which a pretty blonde girl dressed in black and white, her hair tied into an intricate arrangement on her head, collected breakfast meals from a dumb waiter and arranged them on trays, placing metal lids over them to keep everything warm. She turned suddenly, and embarrassed to have been caught looking, I moved briskly on.

I passed a number of rooms to my left, perhaps five or six, most of which were empty and containing the same decor as my own. A very old lady with thin white hair occupied one of them, sitting motionless in her armchair wearing a pink dressing gown. I imagined her looking out at the swing in the same way I had, only for her it would represent something far more poignant – a remembrance of a swing she once used in her own back garden seventy-odd years ago, events from her childhood. Memories of peace, before the world wars, or possibly after.

Opposite the old lady's room was a sitting-room with bright blue walls and large windows, forming a panoramic view of Jesmond's high street, Osborne Road, already jammed with traffic.

Beyond the high redbrick walls of the hospital people were walking with attaché cases and briefcases, some in suits, others in deliberately torn flares and donkey jackets and brightly coloured Parka jackets.

In white cupboards to the right I found painting materials and various expensive-looking ceramic bowls and crystal vases. I also found stationery, large pieces of rough, varicoloured paper, which I remembered I had used in primary school. Was

130

this a clue that somehow indicated the vital importance of my past, that I might find something significant back there? I remembered the Divine training, and how I'd thought upon leaving St Luke's that Newcastle was to be the place where everything came together. And there I was last night thinking of rehabilitation ...

At the end of the corridor was a lounge. It was empty. In the four corners of the room were tables, one of them for table tennis, the others surrounded by chairs. There were large windows all around the room, and to the left behind a mahogany table were a few shelves of books and games, Trivial Pursuit, Monopoly and so on. In a far corner were green couches and in the centre of the room was a large TV with a long wooden table, two couches and armchairs at either side. The armchairs had high backs to them like royal thrones.

The table tennis table in the corner looked fairly new, unlike the battered old thing at St Luke's. But beside the table tennis, I noticed something curious. I walked closer, just to be certain.

It appeared to be an exact match to one of the wardrobes I had seen in Hartlepool General – the same colour, the same fixtures, fitted into the wall. I was sure that it must contain my new identity. Maybe all of this so far – the wonder of Hartlepool General, the terror of St Luke's – was simply to ascertain various aspects of my character. In this way, these people could equip me with everything I would need in order to conduct my Divine activities. And this would happen to each of the other saints, too.

I imagined the luxurious fabrics that lay behind the door, remembering the brightly coloured lime greens, purples and oranges that I had seen in Hartlepool General. But there was one problem – the door was locked. I looked about for a key, but couldn't find it. On the table in front of the TV were some cigarettes and a lighter, but nothing more.

I went back to my room and found my mother there sorting out my bathroom, arranging my toothbrush, hairbrush and aftershave on the side, leaving the rest of the things in my cream-coloured wash-bag, 'Man's Natural Balance' printed upon it in big green letters.

As I sat down and flicked through the early morning television, presenters laughing amongst themselves and discussing money, housework and celebrity gossip, my breakfast arrived, carried in by the pretty blonde girl. I felt embarrassed to be waited upon by someone whose age was so close to mine. She was tall and self-assured, and to my relief never once looked into my eyes as she placed the tray on my table and swivelled it round so that I could eat my breakfast without leaving the armchair.

As she glided out of the room I guessed she must be 20 or 21. I imagined her going to college or university, that she may even talk about me to her friends. I wondered if she was at all ashamed to be working in such a place as this. I ate my bacon and egg with a renewed appreciation for the efforts people such as herself made for people like me. I was determined not to leave a morsel so as to avoid being disrespectful. I thought of Wilma at St Luke's making the breakfast each day and wondered how I could have been so cruel and idiotic to think she had laced it with poison.

After breakfast, Sheila and a short, elderly man wearing a dark-blue pinstriped suit, white shirt and maroon tie came into the room. I was still sat in the armchair so they both sat on the bed. The elderly gentleman had a head that was mostly devoid of hair, though some existed in snowy white around the fringes of his scalp. He wore thick-rimmed, old-fashioned spectacles. His face was red and jolly, and close up I saw his shirt was white, with fine red and blue stripes.

'James, this is Doctor Norton,' said Sheila, sprightly and radiant despite the fact that it was still early morning.

'Pleased to meet you,' I said, shaking the old man's surprisingly strong right hand.

'Yes, pleased to meet you. I understand you've come from St

Luke's in Middlesbrough, is that right?' he asked.

'Yes, I've come here because I didn't like it there.'

'No, your mother just told me she wasn't happy with the treatment you'd received. I'll have to warn you that, reading over Dr Anderson's notes, I may need some time to find the right combination of medication to make you better. Your particular illness is very difficult to treat. Have you been sleeping, by the way?'

'I slept last night and the night before, but I've missed a few nights.'

'Right. So you could maybe do with a sleeping tablet to stabilise things. We'll sort that out. How about hallucinations? Are you still hearing things, or has that gone away?'

I was suddenly on guard. He was trying to meddle with the instructions I'd been receiving from God, just like Dr Randall. I decided to play it all down.

'No. That all wore off a few days ago. But I never really had many hallucinations.' Dr Norton fixed me with a small, pale-blue gaze that seemed to smile like Paul Newman's.

'I see. But I should warn you that recognising your own illness is a vital part of recovery. It's when you find the insight that things are not quite right that you're on your way to getting better, and not before. You'll know when you're starting to turn the corner. You're not well, lad. But I'll get you better, you can count on that.' He slapped me reassuringly on the knee and rose, Sheila smiling and towering above me, her white teeth flashing. I was left wondering what he had meant by 'not well', hoping that this did not mean I would be there for another week or so.

After drinking the last of the small pot of tea, I picked up my tray and carried it back to the kitchen, noticing the doctor and nurse make their way up the corridor and into another of the rooms.

The blonde waitress smiled as I placed down the tray. She had clear, hazel eyes which seemed a little self-deprecating as

133

they occasionally shifted to the floor. They didn't stay still for long.

'Thanks a lot,' she said in a gentle, Geordie accent.

I made my way down to the lounge. My mother was sat in one of the high-backed armchairs sipping tea and watching *Good Morning*. Richard and Judy were with a large woman in a plum-coloured crushed-velvet dress who was talking about how to make relationships last.

'Hi, James,' she said, as I sat down in the armchair beside her, 'did you have a nice breakfast?'

'Yeah, it was lovely. The waitress is very pretty, isn't she? I carried the tray back to the kitchen for her.'

'Good lad, that was nice of you. Yes, the people are all nice. Would you like some more tea?'

'Yes, please.' My mother's thoughts seemed elsewhere, far away. She began pouring the tea and I looked around to my right at the wall, which concealed the wardrobe. I pondered where they might have hidden the key.

'What do you think of Dr Norton then?' she asked, handing me a full cup. 'He's nice, isn't he?'

'Yes, I like him.'

'He told me you're going to have to try to relax and get more sleep. That way you'll get better quicker.'

'Yes. But I slept OK last night.'

'I know, but let's see if you can do it more often. We're all so worried about you, James. We want you home.' I watched as she sipped her tea slowly. 'I'm sorry, darling, I need to go after I've finished this. I've got some jobs to do. But I'll come back every day to visit, probably lunchtimes. And when you start to get better, Dr Morgan says you'll be able to have some other visitors.'

'Great.'

We drank the tea, and I walked around the room, eventually settling by the window opposite the wardrobe, looking out through the dark evergreens at the road, a church spire and the

the rooftops of houses and hotels in the distance. The old church wall and the spire silhouetted against the skyline looked like battlements. At ground-level I watched a student slouched forward against a driving wind, which wheezed around the edge of the double-glazed windows. His multi-coloured scarf billowed classically behind him, his modern red record bag with its strap across his chest reminding me of the poster at St Luke's, my red shirt reflecting in the metallic stripe across the figure. I watched him until he went out of sight behind the evergreens, his mop of black hair blowing freely about in the breeze.

Soon my mother rose and began collecting together the cups and saucers on her tray. After taking this back to the kitchen, she returned to the lounge with her overnight case and put it down to hug me.

'You take care,' she whispered in my ear, 'and I'll see you tomorrow.'

'See you.'

I watched her walk briskly down the corridor, her silvery, ankle-length raincoat sweeping out behind her. She went briefly into the glass-walled office and I heard her voice and laughter, then saw her move across to the lift, out of sight.

I sat and watched Richard and Judy present their various experts, a GP taking phone calls and giving advice to depressed housewives, a gay fashion expert describing the latest trends and presenting them with the assistance of glowing young models.

I became aware of steadily approaching footsteps and turned to see Sheila, who smiled and drifted into the lounge and sat beside me. She gave me some tablets and a glass of water, and I drank them down. I still felt aggrieved at having to do this, but remembering the words of the doctor, I knew there was no other way to get home.

'Oooh, I'd like a dress like that,' Sheila said, looking at an emerald green ball gown worn by a cute blonde model with her hair in ringlets, twirling around on the screen, 'do you think you could buy me one when you make your first million?' I smiled and she laughed gently, then drifted back down the corridor with the empty glass.

A vacuum cleaner started up behind me and I turned to see two women in pink uniforms, one of them dusting the small table by the office, a taller woman hoovering the blue corridor carpet with brisk movements of her arms. Richard and Judy's show ended and I flicked around the channels, settling on a boring programme with political commentators sitting round a table discussing John Major's Prime Ministerial weaknesses.

14

I ate lunch in the lounge – a bowl of fresh tomato soup and a ham sandwich. A kindly, middle-aged waitress named Linda brought it through, and meeting her was a joyous break from the hour of solitude that passed immediately before.

Soon after I had placed my finished tray in the kitchen and returned to the lounge, a strongly built man with a grey beard and a number two shave job on his hair came into the room, walking like a hardened cowboy who had just got off his horse. He carried a video cassette in his hand and went over to the video recorder on the floor, took the video cassette from its sleeve and crouched to put it in the machine. He sat on the couch to my left and sighed, switching the channel to 0.

The figure of Mohammed Ali came into view. The man beside me ran a hand over his beard. The video was a recording of the *Rumble in the Jungle*, and I now recognised George Foreman, so different with hair. I'd seen him boxing a couple of months before, on one of his comebacks, fat and bald. But here he was, mean and lean, hammering away at Ali in the early rounds, pinning Ali against the ropes.

'I take it you like boxing then?' I asked, observing the man's eager eyes, transfixed upon the screen.

'Aye. Too much though, mate. That's what I'm 'ere for. Anger management. You?' The man had a deep, threatening voice, and as he spoke, he did not move his eyes away from the screen. He seemed to be shifting his bulk ever closer, as though about to be sucked into it.

'Oh, they think I got spiked with LSD ... but it might be a scam to keep me in for testing and stuff ...'

'Nor, I didn't mean what're ya in for, I mean do ya like boxin'? I'm not into 'earin' people's personal stuff. None of my

137

business, know what I mean?'

'Suppose. Sometimes I watch the boxing, if there's someone like Naseem Hamed or Frank Bruno fighting. I prefer other sports though.' He turned his head to look at me for the first time, his brown eyes bloodshot and angry, but not with me. It was like looking into the eyes of a man who's just lost a lot of money on the races and feels like punching someone to release the pressure. Then he turned his head back to the screen and shook it.

'Can't beat it, man, can't beat it. Look at that – Foreman's got 'im right? No chance of Ali comin' back. He's bloody finished. But no.' We watch Foreman hammering away in the fourth round, the blows raining down on Ali, his face screwing up, searching for that famous self belief, that inner strength. I nodded slowly in agreement. There was a message in Ali's performance for us all, a lesson in human endurance. He had set an example with this comeback fight, a benchmark not only for boxers, or sportsmen, not only for African Americans, but for the whole of mankind. 'He just puts up with it and puts up with it, like 'e's doin' it on purpose. But 'e's not. Those punches fuckin' 'urt. Foreman was an 'eavy puncher. An' then Ali knocks 'im out in the eighth.'

We watched the whole fight and then the man took the tape out of the recorder and put it carefully back in its case.

'I'm Alan by the way,' he growled, grinning with yellow teeth and holding out a muscular, scar-covered hand.

'I'm James.'

'James,' he repeated, picking the cigarettes and lighter from the table and putting them in his pocket, 'pleased to meet ye, son.'

I watched him walk heavily down the corridor and into one of the rooms close to the lounge on the right. The door closed with a bang.

The afternoon drifted on. I walked down the corridor and met the receptionist, who was busily typing away in her office beside the lift. She was quietly spoken, with a plump, cheerful face. She took off her spectacles, stood and chatted with me for some time, occasionally pulling the sides of her blue and green tartan jacket together, as if to conceal a figure that was not so overtly bulky as she may have thought.

'It's lovely to have such a nice, cheery young man as you on the ward, James. There's usually so many depressed people in here who have been through terrible divorces and such like. The nurses have told me what you've been through. You'll be alright, son. Just make sure you do what the nurses tell you to and you'll be alright. I'm Maureen, by the way.'

'Pleased to meet you, Maureen. I'll let you get on with your work.'

'Oh, that's no problem. Any time you want a chat, you know where I am. It's nice to have a break sometimes.'

I went into the nurses' office, noticing a middle-aged woman I had not met before sitting behind the desk. As I walked in she looked up from her paperwork and smiled.

'Oh, hello! I was just gonna come an' see ye after I'd finished this. I'm Lizzie.' Lizzie had a rich Northumberland accent, which reminded me of my friend Ian Lefting, from a small village near Morpeth. I mentioned his name. 'Oh, aye. Live not far from there. They've got a cattery now 'aven't they?'

'Yes, I think so,' I said, shaking her hand. 'Strange that you know them. They haven't got many neighbours.'

'Well, I'm one of them,' she said, smiling broadly. Her hair was dark brown and coiled into springlike curls, giving her a lively countenance. Her eyes were blue and knowing, her skin intermittent with freckles. 'So, you've been doin' alright so far, haven't you? I'll just get your tablets ...'

I followed her down the corridor, wishing I had never bothered to come into the office. She entered a door by the kitchen and opened a cabinet above using one of the keys from the bunch she produced from her pocket. She then arranged the various bottles and carefully counted out the tablets, handing them to me in a plastic cup.

'Now, do you want to go and take them with some water or something?'

I went into the kitchen and poured out some milk, drinking the tablets down and feeling the thrilling sensation of the ice cold milk. I was eager to make a good impression on all of the nurses in order to get home as soon as possible, and I knew that any protests I made regarding tablets would only set my release date back ever further.

After becoming bored in the lounge, and failing to find any books on the shelves that would hold my attention, I went back to my room. I found my Walkman in a cupboard beside the bed, which I noticed fastened shut with a magnet. I sat in the armchair and listened to Nat King Cole's perfect voice, certain that I would be as sensible as he when I fell in love.

I looked up at the white clouds, which seemed to swoop low above the earth, at their contrast with the bright blue of the sky. I looked at the pale grey stone of the house opposite, the brick outline of the flue of its large Victorian chimney running all the way down the back of its three floors, the part of the house that faced my window.

I watched curiously. The flue looked like a join, as if it had more of a purpose than merely to syphon off the harmful smoke of a coal fire. I looked up and admired the building's grand architecture. I tried in vain to see through the windows. As I watched, the whole house moved an inch or so towards my window. I blinked, and took my earphones out. Everything was silent, everything was still. The house stood upright in Victorian correctness, motionless, as if mocking my latest whimsy. I imagined the two small windows were eyes, the long, ornate flue a nose, one of the lines of mortar a pair of thin lips frowning at the edges.

Then it moved forward again, and this time I heard a sound of grinding cement as the building lifted and was moved as if by enormous invisible hands towards me, the ground shaking and a sound like thunder as the house was moved forward. My eyes fell on the windows, the eyes of the house. They seemed to glint with flashes of sunlight. The house moved an inch at a time, an inevitable progression along a seemingly predestined line.

Suddenly I remembered something and ran down the corridor as fast as my feet would carry me. I looked from the window by the table tennis table. The church spire. Or rather, the castle turret. I looked up at the jutting pieces of stone that had at first reminded me of a medieval castle wall. As I studied the landscape, it all became remarkably clear. It was evident that the rooftops of all of the nearby houses could conceivably be forced to interconnect. I thought of the magnet on the cupboard. Perhaps the houses were being pulled together by a magnetic field, the true invisible hand that had shifted the house.

I sped back down the corridor and into my room. My heart jumped against my ribs, and I looked across at the house in horror. The flue would crush against my room. My room would be one of the joins of this new castle. I could see it now – in the distance lay row upon row of large houses with identically constructed roofs. Some of these, it seemed, were to be sacrificed and made into castle walls. And as I heard the sound of masses of crumbling concrete, the houses came ever closer. The image of such an enormous stone construction being moved forward as simply as a lump of Lego seemed preposterous.

Terrified, I went back down to the lounge, trying not to appear conspicuous. Maybe the nurses were all in on it, Lizzie, Sheila and the rest – perhaps even the waitresses and cleaners. But it was an important change. It was the vision gone wrong. Westmoreland had begun to develop in a way I had never conceived. Someone had evidently taken over in the time I was in St Luke's, and my visionary powers were now of little use. Indeed, I felt powerless as I sat in a high-backed chair, my legs and feet shaking uncontrollably, my mind looping back on itself, over and over, trying to find a logical explanation for what I had just seen.

Lizzie came with another tablet, oblivious to the thunderous sounds, and insisted I take a tablet. I eventually managed to take it, though she had to keep refilling my glass with water as my hand shook so violently that it kept spilling on the floor.

Soon everything calmed and I began watching *Countdown* in complete relaxation, with no thought of previous events, and indeed little recollection of them. Memories came only briefly, and too brief to grasp successfully. It seemed curious how quickly the vision faded.

As evening came, the clouds flattened out and the sun died an orange death on the horizon, turning gradually pink, the clouds taking on these pigmentations like chameleons melting into the background. Then the sky turned mauve, and I sat entranced by the spectacle, viewing it through a tired haze. I stood and watched the church spire's dark outline, religion standing bold above the world as it revolved beneath its watchful eye.

As night cast its dark blanket over everything, I closed the curtains and could smell dinner cooking and hear pots clattering in the kitchen. I realised there were only three patients on the ward: myself, Alan, the boxing enthusiast, and the old lady. Going down the corridor I stopped in her doorway, fascinated by her motionless form. She just stared on and on into the blackness without even turning on a light, as though there were no distinction between night and day. Her owl-like glasses caught the light from the corridor in a thin cusp upon the inside rim of her spectacles, but the only outward sign she gave of being alive was in the faint rise and fall of her slight bosom. Other than that she was nothing more than a still life, like one of Damien Hirst's prize-winning exhibits. Her inactivity distressed me, and I was saddened to think that all human life must eventually come to this, a hopeless inertia. I looked on her closed eyes and open mouth and felt I was wasting my youth, that I was observing rather than participating. Yeats's immortal lines swam vividly toward me.

When you are old and grey and full of sleep,
And nodding by the fire, take down this book,
And slowly read, and dream of that soft look
Your eyes had once, and of their shadows deep ...

Opening one of the drawers in her wardrobe, her shadows came to me in a whirl of images: a picture of her long lost husband, killed in a war, in full naval dress, waving on his final departure to sea. Her mother and father peered from a small frame, their image all but faded in the photograph, brown with age. This contrasted with a colourful print of her grandchildren, stood all in a line like smiling prime suspects, smartly dressed, with herself in the middle, maybe taken on her 80th birthday.

Hearing a cough, I turned suddenly to see the aged eyes upon me, but no word escaped her lips. She smiled slightly, wrinkling her face, and suddenly I recalled a time when I had touched my own grandmother's face and asked her how she had managed to acquire such *cracks* ...

I felt a pang of guilt for prying into the poor woman's world and waking her up, so, smiling apologetically, I slid the drawer shut and crept out of the room. Linda was laying out the trays for dinner. In my bathroom, I switched on the light and examined my own eyes. Dark crevices were in evidence beneath them, and I realised why I had automatically avoided them the previous evening, probably at around the same time as this. The twilight hour, the death of day. I fell into the black chasms of dilated pupils, which almost eclipsed the dark brown irises so that only a mere millimetre of colour was visible around their circumference. They were eyes that looked afraid,

afraid of shadows that lay ahead, afraid that all they might view in the future would be from the confines of shadow, from inside this hospital. Afraid of becoming old and grey within its confines.

'Hello, James!'

I jumped, disturbed by the sound of Linda's voice and the rattle of her tray, but was glad to turn away from the mirror and exit the bathroom. 'I'll just put your tray on here for you,' she said, placing it gently upon the table.

'Thanks, Linda,' I said, and she smiled and walked out, clearing her throat on her way out characteristically, like a full stop on a job completed.

I had almost forgotten ordering the leek soup and roast beef and Yorkshire pudding, which lay steaming before me. But I enjoyed the meal, and drinking my tea afterwards felt much invigorated. It had been a long day, and I yawned and stretched and took my tray back to the kitchen. Still a little hungry, I asked if I could have some cheese and biscuits, and Linda pointed to a small ready-prepared tray and thanked me for bringing the larger one back.

As I ate, Lizzie and Sheila wheeled a white trolley into my doorway. I heard the tablets dropping into a plastic cup, making a 'plink' like the sound of heavy rain droplets falling into puddles. Lizzie approached my armchair and handed them to me, though she did not look so pleased to see me as before, her forehead corrugated with vexation.

'I've heard that you've been going in and out of people's rooms, James. We want you to feel at home, but don't go into other people's rooms. You wouldn't like it if people came into your room and messed about with your things now, would you?' My heart sank. The old lady had obviously complained. Sheila's face showed similar vexation as Lizzie's from the doorway, but the corrugations were not so deep. Her black, neatly plucked eyebrows had dipped into the shape of a wave.

'No, I suppose not.'

'No. Anyway, make sure you don't do it again, and we'll forget all about it.'

Lizzie marched back out into the corridor, and the trolley rolled away.

After watching dull episodes of *Emerdale* and *Coronation Street* alone in my room, I met the night nurses Peter and Anna in the lounge. It seemed the Nuffield was similar to St Luke's in only one respect: the handover was at eight o'clock.

Peter was a tall, craggy-faced man, clean-shaven, with grey-black hair that had turned white at the edges. He smelled of the rolling tobacco he frequently smoked, rolling briskly and with surprising delicacy with his large hands. Anna was short with jet-black hair that she wore in a neat bob, the darkness of which was in stark contrast to her deathly-pale complexion. She had sharp blue eyes and a cackling laugh, which all in all made me suspicious that she might be some sort of witch. I remarked upon this the moment I met her. She immediately laughed, leaning back in her high-backed chair. I was sat in the other, Peter on a couch, crouched forward arranging Golden Virginia in a cigarette paper and watching the corridor, revealing tobacco-stained teeth in a wolfish grin.

'Eeeh! Everyone says that, don't they, Peter?' laughed Anna.

'Aye. All ya'd need's a broom an' ye could fly away!'

We all laughed together, Peter bent double and clutching his knees, Anna's back pressed hilariously into her chair. After we had all calmed, and got our breath back, Anna suggested that I might want to take my tablets and head for bed.

'Actually, yes, I feel quite tired now,' I said.

'Right then, let's get your tablets.'

She took me down to the little room near the kitchen and selected from the cupboard the tablets indicated beneath my name in the medical notes, attached to a red clipboard.

'There's a new tablet for you to take this evenin', darlin' – it's called Zopiclone ... It says 'ere you've had trouble sleepin' and this is what the doctor's prescribed for you. Okay?'

I shrugged my shoulders. 'That's no problem.'

I took the tablets she gave me and drank them down in the kitchen with plenty of orange juice. Then I headed back to my room, waving to Anna, who was heading back up to the lounge. I wanted to rejoin them but felt too drained to do anything other than sleep. Before climbing into bed I pulled back the curtain slightly. The house opposite was quite still, and the distance between it and my window had increased so that it was now the same as when I had first arrived from Middlesbrough. It was as if nothing had happened, as if I had imagined everything. I looked up at the motionless grey outline, partially lit by a dim floodlight and a silver slice of moon.

15

At 3.30 a.m. I awoke and walked down to the lounge to find Peter with his eyes closed, Anna reading a copy of *Cosmopolitan*. I sat and giggled uncontrollably at Peter, whose weary face seemed somehow hilarious. I was at the sleep/wake border, which the medication contributed to and allowed me to live inside, so that consequently everything seemed ridiculous and madcap. Anna looked even more witch-like than before, and she cackled when I reintroduced the joke about the broom. I even began to search about the room for it, certain that it must be somewhere, giggling profusely. But soon she began to rustle her magazine, and it was obvious that her impatience was growing. Peter opened his eyes.

'James, I need a rest. I can't rest when you're up and about.'

What was this? Were our energy levels somehow interconnected? Was it possible that as I slept, Peter's energy became restored? Perhaps they were indeed supernatural agents. Maybe Peter was a vampire, maybe he wanted my blood. But strangely I felt no fear – only a drowsy, drunken-minded hilarity, a dreamlike, half-asleep inertia. And suddenly Peter's tired utterance provoked belated laughter from me, as it replayed itself in my mind.

But now Peter stood, groaning deeply as his knee joints cracked and he stretched his arms high into the air. He reminded me of the poet Ted Hughes, with his craggy skin and greyish hair. I decided to do as he said, and walked briskly back to my room, the pair of them softly uttering the words: 'Goodnight, James!' in voices that seemed laden with enchantment and strangely inflected vowels.

In the morning I watched the news four times before breakfast, between 6.30 a.m. and 8.30 a.m., in an effort to improve my concentration. I figured if I could sit through four episodes of the news and remember what I had seen, then my concentration would have shown improvement. Moreover, the news stories seemed to me rather fascinating at that particular moment in time. It was February 19, and an IRA device had 'accidentally' exploded on board a bus. I watched the pictures as a man named Kevin Mitchell, a barman at Zola's Bar near the blast site, described how he rushed out to try to help. 'I saw two people blown apart in the bus. It made me feel quite sick. The top of the bus was peeled back like a sardine can.'

I watched the man's desperate face and the wrecked vehicle and felt a remarkable sense of guilt. What had I been doing yesterday afternoon? Watching buildings moving. No, worse than that – I had been *imagining* that I was watching buildings moving. And meanwhile, 300 hundred miles away, two people had died and seven badly injured by a bomb. I realised for the first time that I had managed to create a certain distance between myself and the world. I had become too introverted to care about what was happening, lost interest in watching the news or reading newspapers. I decided that this had to change.

Next, Judi Dench appeared wearing a beautiful black sequined ball gown, receiving an unprecedented double of Best Actress and Best Actress in a Musical at the Lawrence Olivier Awards. I listened to her graceful speech and watched her calm demeanour. There seemed a grandeur about her that belonged to a bygone era, full of old-fashioned manners and decency. A story on Michael Jackson came next, in his white Brit Award suit singing 'Earth Song', the voiceover of the newscaster intimating allegations that Jackson was attempting to 'play God' in his all-white get-up. A demented Jarvis Cocker ran on stage at this point, screams and jeers from the crowd faintly audible over the presenter's voice. The Brits were always full of quaint little incidents and controversial publicity stunts. It was one thing that never seemed to change.

When Lizzie brought in my tablets, I had just finished

watching the news for a fourth time, and felt satisfied that I had managed to do so, though my joints ached from the effort required to suppress my body's constant hyperactive intentions. I asked Lizzie if I could order a *Guardian* every morning to keep in touch with events and give me something to read, and she agreed to do this for me.

'That's a good idea you know, James. One of the things you'll need to work on is getting your concentration back to normal.'

I listened to the growing levels of activity beyond my room. I heard Peter and Anna saying their goodbyes after the handover, their voices drifting over from the direction of the lift, then echoing around its metallic interior before the doors closed.

Laura looked miserable as she brought in my breakfast, her doll-like features downcast as she entered the room, sighing gently as she placed down the tray. I pointed to the grey skies and suggested that perhaps the weather had something to do with her mood.

'Aye, I always feel miserable when it's dull and grey. Gets me down.'

The weather forecast came on after the adverts and promised cold northeasterly winds and a minimum temperature of minus two degrees Celsius. I looked out over the window pane and saw thin patches of ice on the ground.

'Make sure you don't slip on the ice, Laura.' She smiled and left the room, pointing to the black trainers on her feet that had taken the place of high heels.

As I drank my tea and dipped salty smoked bacon into the yolk of a fried egg, Lizzie brought in a newspaper, along with a mountain of mail, all of which she dumped on my unmade bed.

'Are they all for me?!' I asked, shocked to see so many envelopes.

'Yes, plenty for you to read. You'll probably never get to read any of that newspaper after all,' Lizzie said, turning and

149

walking out once more.

My hands shook as I picked up the pile of letters and searched through them. I did not recognise most of the handwriting, so picked out a white envelope at random and tore it open. Inside was a card bearing the words:

I Know You Think I'm a Bit of a Mug
But All I Want Is To Give You A Hug

on the front of it. Inside it I recognised Rachel Lockwood's distinctive, schoolgirlish hand, wishing me well, with lots of little x's.

At that moment, a tiny glass figure caught my eye. Perhaps Sylvia Plath would have called it a homunculus. I sat transfixed as it stood there by my teacup, not more than a centimetre tall, looking up at me. Daylight shone upon his glassy, see-through skin. He had a featureless face, no eyes or nose, just a blank, glass oval. I watched in disbelief as the figure ran along the length of my table about half a metre from my face. Dr Norton came into the room as the tiny figure turned to run another length, and I commented on the glass figure before me.

'Look! Can't you see it?' Dr Norton leaned forward at my insistence and examined the exact area where the figure now stood motionless, looking back at the doctor.

'No, I can't see anything. It must be a visual hallucination. Oh, such a lot of post!' He shifted some of the letters and sat on the bed. Sheila stood near the doorway, looking concerned. 'Is it still there now?' I had not taken my eye off it. But suddenly it ran to the edge of the table and jumped off, minuscule fragments of glass or whatever substance he was made of shattering and disappearing into the carpet, and the figure had gone.

'No. He just committed suicide.'

'Right ... You know, these hallucinations won't last forever.

Once the tablets have taken full effect they will stop. They must be happening less and less now, are they not?'

'But it was there ...' I looked at the building opposite that I had been hypnotised by the day before, the row of houses that had been moving towards me, inch by inch. The doctor would be sure to disbelieve me on that one, too. It was time to imagine the impossible – that none of it was real. I made a compromise with my ideologies. 'I'm starting to realise that they aren't real. Shakespeare portrayed his character Macbeth as having an hallucinatory imagination. Maybe I've got one too.'

'Well, that's very possible. With your illness, visual hallucinations are not uncommon. It could be that when you were spiked with LSD this sent a chain of reactions off, and subsequently caused you to see things that would normally be part of your imagination. However, we'll get you sorted, lad.' He slapped my knee and laughed jovially. 'I don't like to keep patients here for long. You belong out there in the real world. Did you sleep well?'

'Oh, not really. I woke up at three or half-three. But I got back to sleep.'

'Ah, that's encouraging.' He took off his glasses and rubbed his eyes and forehead. His face was a little red with the strain of work. But as he was working through his late sixties, it was evident that he was a workaholic. Suddenly, he leapt to his feet.

'Right, come on, Sheila! See you tomorrow, James. You can read all your love letters now.' And then he walked away, chuckling quietly with Sheila.

I looked vacantly at the card from Rachel that was still in my hands, then tossed it across the room. I picked out another, an enormous A4-sized 'Get Well' card. Inside it were the signatures of all the girls from Teesside High School that were my own age, with lots of hugs and kisses. I looked incredulously at the various personal messages, the writing of girls I knew only vaguely from parties, others whom I'd never met but whose names I recognised.

Another envelope contained a long letter from Ben Tillett, scribbled during 'another boring German lesson'. He expressed a concern for my health and a hope that the drugs I'd been spiked with were exciting. (Ben was into anything that was, as he put it, 'exciting'.) I smiled and opened another envelope, this time a small rectangular thing. Inside was a short note from a businessman in London, 'I read your case in the newspaper and was appalled ... the world needs more brave young people like you ...', along with the man's business card and a cheque for ten pounds, signed to me.

I stared at the cheque for some minutes, amazed that someone I had never met would want to send me money, confused as to what this strange message could mean. I found a little news clipping detailing the drug spiking incident similarly worded to that of the *Sun* article I'd read a week before. Maybe it was true after all, and this guy felt sorry for me. I looked at the pile of letters, perhaps a hundred of them. How strange that I was so popular all of a sudden.

I thought of all those long nights alone in my room reading. All those poems I had written in happy solitude since I was seven or eight. All those beatings and taunts I'd taken at school for being quiet and 'different' as my headmaster used to explain it. But as I opened another card and read all the names of my school year, organised by Ben Tillett, Julian Welsh's name amongst them, I felt more isolated than ever.

I also felt bitterness – that these friends and acquaintances had no idea what I was going through, that they probably never would, and they could certainly not understand. Perhaps the whole thing would isolate me further still. Perhaps solitude was something I must get used to, even outside the imprisoning walls of the Newcastle Nuffield. The cards were like little nails smiling at me from their positions on my bed, ready to drive through my skin and remind me of the impending fear of eternal solitude dawning slowly upon me.

I looked down at the names and remembered things. Through the muffled voices of nurses and the boxing enthusiast Alan leaving, shouting goodbye with all the loud triumph of a gorilla being let loose from a cage, I saw the faces of these people and their snide, boyishly waspish remarks. I looked at their spiteful, reluctantly scrawled writing. Only two or three of them were genuine, of that I was sure. The rest were merely hangers-on, part of the bunch that only two years before had encircled me and collectively rubbed my face in the mud and snow, kicked me in the stomach and ribs to mark my 14th birthday. I watched the thin figure stagger back from the past, blind with fury and fear, bruised and broken. I looked down at the names and wondered how he would have regarded such hypocrisy, and whether he would have believed it.

Putting the card quickly to one side to avoid an onrush of anger, I read on. I had cards from old primary school teachers, notes to say that mass would be offered in my name from 30 or 40 church-goers across the country. There were words of hope from a distant relative now living in Egypt, as well as from close family and cousins. A message of encouragement from a cousin in Livingston who had suffered from depression a couple of years before.

My patience wore thin, and I looked wearily across at the card from the lads at Yarm School and stood up angrily, pacing the room. I marched up the corridor to the lounge, rattled the locked fire door and went back to my room. Thinking of their freedom created a new, gnawing misery in imprisonment. I sat in my armchair and stared from the window, imagining the bastards who had tormented me all those years running free through the breeze, playing football and talking to girls.

I decided to take a bath. Taking the towel I had been provided, I went into the office where Lizzie was writing notes. Sheila was carefully filing some papers into a beige cabinet.

'Hi. I was just wondering where the bathroom is? I need a wash.'

'Oh, that's no problem,' said Lizzie, looking up from her notes after finishing a sentence, 'just follow me.'

I followed her up the corridor, and just after the kitchen we turned right into a spacious room containing a white, rectangular bathtub. 'There you are. You've got a towel there I see. And don't pull this red cord unless it's an emergency.' I nodded, and Lizzie smiled and went back down the corridor.

Shutting the door, I put in the plug and ran the bath, the steam rising and the warm vapour from the water relaxing me. I poured in some of the blue Radox bath oil provided, marked 'Detox'. I needed to detox.

Soon the white foam was piling up like floating clouds and I took off my clothes and tested the water with my toe, adding some more cold water. Eventually I got in, engulfed by the water and inhaling the refreshing fumes. Feeling drowsy, I closed my eyes. Through the drowsiness came Rachel's face, her lips mouthing the words: 'all I want is to give you a hug.' I slid my body further into the bath and let myself completely submerge, holding my breath beneath the warm water. A hazy recollection of her with Giles Walder pieced itself together.

I slid my head back out above the water and breathed deeply. I rubbed my eyes. But then as I closed them I felt myself drawn back there on a tantalising mystery trail of memory, searching for clues. Drifting back down the dark pathway to the door of the club.

* * *

The warm air brought a burning sensation to my cheeks as I followed Julian through the door. The music seemed louder than before. I flashed my ticket at the bouncer, and was conscious of everything in slow motion, observing with consummate care. Something was wrong – the van looked suspicious and I knew it. Someone was going to get their drink spiked.

154

I caught up with Julian at the bar where he was hastily ordering another drink.

'Do you want one?' he asked, shouting over the noise.

'Cheers. Here's the money for a pint of cider and one for yourself. I'm just nipping to the bog.'

'Right-o.'

The sign for the Gents hung over a corridor on the side of the bar closest the entrance. I walked past the pretentious banter of sixteen-year-old wannabes, but also a group of older men in their thirties who were stood by the bar looking at the young girls around them. Across the bar I saw Rachel standing alone with a drink in either hand, waiting. I prepared to meet her new boyfriend in the Gents, guessing that this was where he might be. I pulled back the heavy oak door and went in. At a latrine I saw the broad back of Giles Walder, his strawberry-blond hair shaved into a step at the back as was the fashion. I stepped catlike into the empty and only cubicle, taking care that he didn't see me, and slammed the door in frustration, locking it behind me.

As I sat down I heard voices outside, one of them belonging to Giles.

'That's him!' someone said, his voice quivering with excitement. Knuckles hammered against the cubicle door.

'Who?' said Giles.

'You know! The one ...' The unknown voice tumbled into a low whisper. Hurried footsteps followed, and the heavy door opened and slammed shut, leaving a mystified silence.

When I had finished I came out of the cubicle. I looked in the mirror, a little shaky now. I washed cold water over my face and felt a cocktail of fear and anger. But there was something else. My eyes were larger than normal, and I knew what that could mean – drugs. I steadied myself, drying my face carefully with toilet roll, hurrying slightly as another guy I didn't recognise came in. But it was undeniable – an energy surged within me like the heavy bass pulse of the music, throb-

155

bing through the oaken door. I paused in front of it, then went out.

I was through the door and up the stairs as quickly as I could. Suddenly I was telling everyone I could recognise in the dim light, now crowded together in drunken conversation, what I had been told, that someone was due to be spiked, to watch their drinks.

'I was told only yesterday – seriously, be careful … I think there's dealers in here … There'savanoutside … looksabit… suspicious… Iwrotethenumberplatedown…!' I felt the words tearing out of my mouth; I was conscious of my speech uncontrollably gathering pace.

'We – can't – understand – you!' shouted Gaby, her laughter coming to me over the noise, her small eyes gleaming joyfully through black eyeshadow like jewels. Julian was pushing a pint into my hand and looking a little annoyed.

'Where'd you go?'

'The toilet .. something's not right … I'm worried … Look, watch this pint, I need to check something.'

I wasn't safe. I went to the entrance porch and sat watching the van. At that moment it appeared an all-consuming crime machine, come to consume me. The pint Julian gave me could have been spiked without his knowledge. I sat, resolutely waiting for the night to end, for the safety of home. My mind moved ten-to-the-dozen. I felt myself setting off on a rollercoaster, and held on.

* * *

The bubbles crackled quietly as I watched the memories recoil, and the music fade into the distance. I shook tension from my shoulders and breathed deeply. My drowsy eyes fell upon the bottle of bubble bath. 'Detox' – I spoke the word aloud and breathed deeply once more – 'that's what I need to do, I said to myself. And for a few minutes everything drifted away, cocooned in a warm, watery escape.

156

Suddenly there was a banging on the door.

'James! James!'

'Yes! What is it?'

'It's Lizzie. I was banging on your door before but you never heard me. Your lunch is ready, and it's time for you to take some more tablets.'

'Just a minute!'

I got up slowly from the tub, my limbs heavy and relaxed, and began drying myself with the towel.

The afternoon drifted away in a dull haze of chat shows and documentaries. In the evening I ate my meal and went down to the lounge. There I found two men, one of them seated on the couch to the left, who I guessed was around twenty years old, with a cloud of jet-black hair and a constant smile. He was chain-smoking Dunhill cigarettes, lighting a fresh one with the end of his last as I came into the room. Opposite him was a shorter, older man with closely cropped, slightly receding brown hair and small intelligent eyes, the sleeves of his checked shirt rolled up to reveal muscular forearms. His stubble-coated, square-jawed face was flushed and anguish-stricken. He was doing most of the talking, rambling desperately on in the semblance of a northern accent, with occasional interjections from the younger man.

'I said to her, I really, truly, from the bottom of my heart care for you, I would do anything for you. Anything. And what did she do? Went off with another guy!'

'What sort of job's he got?' asked the younger man.

'Oh, he's a lawyer. A lawyer! I mean, of all people. And he's good lookin' as well. But I said to her, you have your life and I have mine. We can't do this without the occasional argument, you know? It's just not possible – every couple argues about something. Alright, she went off with another guy, but you see Robert, that's the problem, she won't take me back 'cos she feels *guilty* ...'

There was a slight pause. Robert took a long, audible drag

on his cigarette and leaned back. The other man looked vaguely up at the ceiling as though wishing for divine aid. I sat down on the high-backed chair to the left, and together the two men looked at me. The older man sat up.

'Hello there, what's your name? I'm Matthew. This is Robert.'

'Hi,' said Robert.

'Hi, I'm James.'

'James, eh? So what's wrong with you? You look a bit young to be in a place like this!' He smiled and the two men laughed a little.

'Yes, I suppose. I'm sixteen. Someone spiked my drink at a party I went to,'

'Ah, the rotten buggers ... or bugger. You pressin' charges?' asked Matthew.

'I'm not sure. Haven't really thought about it – it could all be a lie. They might be just keeping me here and using that story as an excuse.'

'And why would they do that?' He fixed his gaze upon me, piercing pale-blue eyes streaked with tiredness and his own torment. 'You want to take all your tablets on time and get yourself back home. That's the most important thing. I'm in for depression 'cos me bleedin' wife's left me, and poor Robert here's got mild – what is it?'

'Schizophrenia – it comes and goes.' He was still smoking. It looked like he would go on until the whole packet was gone.

'Can I borrow a cigarette off you?' I asked. He took one from the pack and extended it to me but Matthew took it from him and put it back in the box.

'No, that's something you definitely do not want to start, at your age. Once you have one you'll want twenty.' He sat back and folded his enormous arms, and dropped back into monologue. Robert settled into a new cigarette as though he enjoyed playing the counsellor. I supposed that I was assistant counsellor now that I'd joined the throng. 'I'm thirty-five years old, I own three farms, I provided her with whatever she wanted. A lawyer can't do that! She loves money. I do a little bit of rowing up at Durham, you know, once or twice a week ... and she used to go mad – "You're always out with your mates," she'd say, "spend more time with *me*." ' His voice broke with the final word, and his handsome face creased up, a single tear trickling down a cheek. He held his face in his right hand as if he were suffering from a migraine, rubbing his eyes slowly with his thumb and forefinger, and broke into a sob. Robert ran off down the corridor, cigarette in the corner of his mouth. I stood and tried to console Matthew but he was far away, lost in an intimate hell of regret and fallen dreams.

Shortly, a stockily built nurse I'd never seen before came bustling down the corridor, Robert trailing lazily behind as though he were walking through a stiff breeze. The nurse touched Robert gently on the shoulders and sat in the chair beside me.

'Ow-kay, mucka, take it easy son. You'll make yourself sick!' Matthew looked up suddenly and smiled.

'Why would I be in here if I wasn't sick already?' he said, starting to laugh. 'Where are you from anyway, Sunderland?'

'Aye, mucka. Can't you tell by me accent?'

'Nor, not really, like. Mucka,' Matthew said, imitating her exaggeratedly, and we all laughed. The nurse had a shock of short wavy brown hair and pale skin, and jovial eyes that crinkled up tightly when she laughed, her head falling back, her bulky figure quivering all over.

'I'm Claire by the way. As in Trevor Sin-clair the footballer!' Matthew burst into laughter and the rest of us followed, infectiously over-exaggerated as it was. His laugh resembled that of a child with an uncontrollable giggle. Robert's was more of a laid-back chortle.

We sat back and basked in the aftermath of the laughter, catching our breath. I felt elated, high and happy in a way I had not felt for some time. Looking across at where the wardrobe was situated I felt this was a good time to ask the question that had been bothering me for some time.

'Claire, have you got the key to that wardrobe over there?'

'Wardrobe? Eeeee, he, he, he ...' and they were off again, but this time I couldn't see the joke. 'That's a cupboard, darlin'. Look, I'll show you.'

'You're gonna have some fun with this one, aren't you?' giggled Matthew, his accent more northern in the midst of his hilarity.

Claire smiled back at him and selected a shining silver Yale key from the big bunch in her pocket, and walked with me to the front of it. Paralysed with anticipation, I watched the key turn slowly in the lock. I imagined my new things on the other side of it, new clothes, books, words of instruction. All secretly placed here when no one was looking by another agent of God. I shuffled frantically from foot to foot as the key stuck in the stiff lock, Claire grimacing slightly as she battled with it.

And then it was open. Inside I could see various boxes, some filled with soap, others with cleaning provisions. There were also stacks of white Nuffield towels. But no clothes, no books, no words of instruction. My elation dipped away and I felt the onset of a deep depression spreading through every sinew. It was all in my imagination.

'You see, mucka? Nowt there!' Claire said gently. 'Sorry to disappoint ya, pet.'

I stood motionless for some seconds, staring at all the mundane stuff. It made no sense. But I noticed a cylindrical cavity where no doubt a piece of specially shaped metal could fit, and this could magically transform the contents. Convinced that this piece would at some point be presented to me, I decided to rejoin the comedy club to rediscover that earlier elation.

But soon Matthew was back into a depressive train of thought, back into his lost wife and lost dreams and wondering how he had contrived to let it all go wrong.

'I don't know what I did wrong. I honestly, truly, deeply ...'
The needle kept skipping back to the same area of the vinyl,
and throughout it all Robert smoked on, even Claire lit up,
perhaps to prevent herself from interrupting him, to allow him
to let it all out. She looked at her watch and turned to me.

'Ye better get yerself into bed, pet. James, isn't it? Aye, it's
ten now, so ye'll get a nice sleep in.' Matthew was still talking
to Robert. 'I'll be back in a minute, mucka.'

After taking the tablets, I drifted back to my room, tired but
happier. It struck me that this was rather like a hotel, with
various people coming and going and talking to one another in
comfortable surroundings. As I took off my glasses and placed
them on the side, I looked forward to the next day, and seeing
my new acquaintances again. I paused for a moment and
viewed Monet's version of my room through short-sighted
eyes, and thought about returning to the lounge. Finally I
decided against it, feeling quite at home as I climbed into the
springy bed and lay my head upon the pillow. Matthew's
laughter floated briefly through the air once more, then ended
abruptly.

16

In the morning I awoke rather late and read the *Guardian* in bed. The IRA were denying any involvement in the London bus bombing – 'I am as saddened as anyone else, says Adams' adorned the front page. Despite my wish to learn of world events, I flicked automatically past it all to the Arts section.

Dr Norton came into the room and sat in the armchair, as I was still in bed, and announced that my mother had phoned and told him she would be visiting later.

'She says she had things to sort out yesterday so she had to cancel her visit. But I understand you've not been well. That right?'

I looked downcast at the floor. I knew it was true, but was reluctant to admit it, even to myself. I was certain there must be some logic to all of this, some semblance of unity.

'This is all part of my Divine quest,' I began, searching for the right explanation, 'my Divine training. This must all be a kind of test . . .'

The doctor screwed up his eyes and ran a hand over his forehead. He answered in his usual quiet, rambling tone, which never varied. 'Well, I guess in one way it is a test. You're a very young age for this to happen to. I know I haven't quite got the meds right so far, and for that I am sorry.' He took a deep breath. I noticed he had no chaperone today, no Sheila. 'There is one thing, however. The urine sample taken on the thirteenth of this month has returned from the lab. An unknown substance was found in it, possibly LSD. That would probably explain some of the flashbacks and visual hallucinations. But a urine sample won't stand up in court, even though it is effectively ninety nine per cent certain that you had ingested some form of hallucinogen, and as the blood sample

162

appears to have been lost en route to Liverpool, I have suggested that the police call off their investigation.'

'Sure ... so there was an investigation ...'

'Oh, yes. You see, you need to start facing up to reality, lad. You've been doing some strange things, and indeed you could argue that these strange things have forced themselves upon you. But you must begin to recognize them ...'

The doctor rambled on but my concentration was shot once more, and I was unable to follow the low, rambling nature of his dialogue. The sun had crept out and half-blinded me as I tried to at least appear to be paying attention. But I found his story of a police investigation difficult to believe. It all seemed so far-fetched and fanciful, I much preferred my own version of events. That these visions were true and they had happened to me and me alone. Evidently this was why he could not see the glass man the previous day.

Dr Norton mentioned something about the writers Lord Byron and Virginia Woolf; that their illnesses directly correlated with my own, and suddenly I found myself uncontrollably uttering the words: 'I don't believe you. You're making it all up.'

At this the doctor rose and smiled. 'Believe me, you'll get through this, lad. I'll sort you out,' he said, then slapped me on the back and walked out of the room with characteristic jauntiness.

I washed my face in the sink. The acne had begun to recede, though the skin was by no means clear. The bags beneath my eyes were also healing slowly. I washed my hair and combed it back tightly on my head.

Selecting a fresh, bright-blue shirt from the wardrobe with the yellow Yves Saint Laurent symbol on it, I tucked it into a pair of jet-black jeans, and attached a black belt. I was now so lean that even on the last notch of the belt the jeans were slack by a couple of inches. Walking across to the window, my knees clicked with the Chlorpromazine, and as I stretched them my

163

knuckles did the same, as though releasing tiny demons from secret lairs between the joints.

From the window, I gazed up at the cloud formations, high and white and handsome. I thought of the cupboard and its future transformation into my new belongings and instructions, and wondered where I might find the metal part that would slot into the cylindrical cavity and set this all in motion. It could be that I was to be a doctor after all, like my grandfather. I remembered he once ran Airedale Hospital, wrote a Ph.D. on leukaemia treatment. What if his spirit was being transferred into my own body in time for adulthood?

As I thought of these things and watched the clouds move in myriad shapes against the blue, I heard footsteps behind me and the sound of tablets rattling in a disposable plastic cup. And at that moment the rubber stamp was applied to those thoughts. I observed the clouds form the shape of an enormous white hand outstretched towards me, in the palm of which was a first aid symbol + .

'What you lookin' at, James?' asked Lizzie, standing beside me.

'Look – in the clouds, you see it?'

'I can't see anything,' she said in an annoyingly knowing and bored tone, 'what do you see, more to the point?'

'The hand of God outstretched towards me, see?' I drew the outline on the window with the tip of my right index finger. 'It's holding out a medical symbol toward me. This means God has ordained that every person's health is my concern.'

Lizzie folded her arms. 'I can't see anything. But I would suggest you're hallucinating again, and that it's time you took these tablets. Your breakfast'll be through shortly.'

'I don't need tablets. This is my calling to help others in need.' I felt a great piety wash over me, and was almost embarrassed about it.

Lizzie's voice became softer and more persuasive. 'James, you've got to decide whether you want to get better. Without these tablets you'll get worse, as Dr Norton's told you.'

I took a moment to consider. 'And what do the tablets actually do?' I asked, from my position of medical superiority, testing her skills as a nurse.

'You know what they'll do. They'll help control your mood, to improve your concentration, to calm you down. And they will make you see reality, and not the things that are in your imagination.'

'And what if I don't want to see reality? What if I prefer the truth? Your reality is not the truth. It's the blind leading the blind, the problem of Everyman ...'

'You're not making any sense. Take these tablets or you won't be going home in the near future. You won't be allowed.'

I watched the great hand and the symbol dissolve as the clouds morphed into new formations. The proof had gone, and I felt defeated. I looked at the human palm in front of me and the tablets that were her offering of first aid. So I did as she asked. But I believed what I had seen, and reflected that time would tell which of us was right.

Later I went down to the lounge and found Matthew and Robert sat in the same positions as they were the previous night. Matthew looked tired, but perhaps a little happier. Maybe part of my new role was to help the people of this ward get better. Maybe *that* was why I was here, to guide people out of depression.

'Hey, James,' said Matthew. 'How are you today?'

'I'm good, thanks,' I replied, 'it's a lovely day.'

'Yes,' said Robert, the two of them turning their heads wearily to gaze through the distant windows. 'But it's so bright it hurts my eyes,' he complained, rubbing at the already dark patches beneath and around them.

'We 'ad a late one last night James. Or should I say an early one! What time was it we got to bed, Rob?'

'Oh ... four, I think,' he said, stretching noisily.

'Ah, well. And you got a good night's sleep then?' asked Matthew.

'Yeah. Slept in, in fact.'

'Good lad. Well, do you fancy a run out, Rob? I fancy a quick pint before I have a nap. I'll take you downtown in the Range Rover.'

'Right-o,' said Rob, his black hair ruffled on his head. Matthew looked neat and tidy and freshly shaved. I imagined them entering a bar, where anyone looking at them would think they were just regular guys on their lunch break.

'Can I come? I could just drink Coke,' I pleaded.

'No, I don't think you're allowed – I asked Lizzie earlier. Otherwise of course you could. But we'll be back later. Right, Rob!' And as they left the room I felt that familiar sense of rejection and solitude.

I stood up and stretched, and walked over to the window beside the table tennis. I watched people going to and fro about their everyday business, and tried to imagine where they were going and where they had come from, and wanted to be with them, to be doing the same fascinating things such as going to school, doing the shopping, taking the baby round the block in the pram ... I watched cars speeding up and down the high street, police cars chasing after someone with their blue lights flashing. I wondered what drives these people, what is it that motivates them to do these things? Why bother? The relentlessness of it all, the lack of significant variation. But as I watched I realised how infinitely more fascinating their lives were than my own, and how I squeezed every last drop of detail out of my existence on this ward in order that it should seem fascinating. Perhaps this is how I visualised things – by willing them into being.

By late afternoon the sky had clouded over, and as I sat in my room listening to Nat King Cole watching water droplets hitting the window to form intricate patterns, I heard the elevator doors open, and my mother's voice.

'Hi, Lizzie!' she said, and a couple of seconds later, the office door closed. I crept out of my room and saw the back of her head as she sat opposite the nurse, who was frowning and shaking her head slowly, and emitting low, indecipherable words in a steady lament.

I returned to my music, and in a few minutes my mother appeared in the doorway.

'Hi, James! Sorry I couldn't come to see you yesterday, but I've been so busy ... how's everything going?'

'Oh, I'm OK.'

She sat on my bed, and I remained in the armchair.

'Look, give me a hug,' she said. I rose and sat for some minutes in a close embrace. I felt like a child again, or a new pet that needed training. 'Listen, Dr Norton's going to try some new medication on you, and if it works, you'll be allowed visitors. And then maybe a visit home.' She spotted the pile of cards, and her expression brightened. 'Dear me, look at all the post you've got! Did you get some from the family?'

'Yes. And some from people I've never even met.'

'Isn't that nice? And I've got some more here that came to the house. Shall we go down to the lounge and open them? And we'll make some tea.'

'Yeah, let's do that.'

My mother went back in to see Lizzie whilst I went into the kitchen. I took one of the large stainless steel teapots from the cupboard and found some tea-bags, filling the pot with hot water from the large metal boiler, placing it on one of the ready-made trays laid out for visitors. They were each set for one, so I added another cup and saucer before taking it through. At last I had found a role that was meaningful.

We opened the mail, which mostly consisted of communications from well-wishers, and three more cheques, each for £10. Amongst them were letters from religious organisations offering help and spiritual advice. One of my old primary school teachers, a Kenyan woman named Kathryn Neduvelil, wrote that she had persuaded her Catholic church to offer mass in my name. I remembered when I was five or six years old and she had told the class that all of her hundred or so saris fit perfectly into a small cupboard. And I remembered how I used to stop doing my maths and watch her marking, imagining her rolling the saris up into tiny balls so as to fit them all into her little cupboard.

Drinking the tea, we each sat in bewildered silence. There were over 80 letters and cards, to put with the hundred or so I had already received.

'Well, you can't say nobody cares about you, James. You'll have to get these up on the wall. There's some Blu Tac in my bag, so we can put them up after we drink this tea if you like.'

I watched my mother's face closely. She looked very tired, the make-up only partially disguising this. The bags beneath her eyes matched my own. But as always she carried herself with confidence and energy, so that beyond her tired appearance I could discern no change to her usual demeanour.

Walking to the window while my mother switched on the six o'clock news and finished her tea, I watched the headlights of cars as they queued behind one another, entering Osborne Road from beyond the conifers to my far right, a constant stream of traffic moving smoothly round the corner and along. I imagined the people within them heading off to great dinner parties in the city, to the theatre or a nice bar. I was one year away from being able to learn to drive, and I looked on this adult-driven stream of lights and understood its mystery, the access that age gives to adulthood, all the dreams that are dreamt up long before its attainment.

We put all of the cards on the wall opposite my bed, 90 in all, and my mother took the letters and said she would take them home so that I could start to reply to them when I was better. I gazed at the neat pattern they made. My mother ran fingers through my hair.

'Right, I'll see you tomorrow, James. Look at that rain! Oh,

168

yes – your father told me to remind you about the Cricket World Cup. It's on Sky Sports every day if you want to watch it.'

'Oh, great. I'll have a look.'

The rain was still hammering against the window, now a liquid black with the darkness. She kissed me on the cheek and picked up her handbag from my bed, then went out and called for the lift, saying a quick goodbye to Lizzie.

Soon after her departure I heard the lift doors open, and rushed out of my room, expecting it to be Matthew and Robert. Instead, the doors opened to reveal a rotund man of around fifty, dressed in an expensive black suit, with greyish hair and large spectacles. He carried a polished black leather briefcase, and as he stepped from the lift there was a great commotion.

'Franson!' exclaimed Lizzie excitedly. 'What you doin' here?' From my secret position, peering out from the frame of my doorway, I could also see Sheila dashing out of the old lady's room at the top of the corridor to greet him. They both hugged him and went into the room beside the office, where the handovers took place. As I crept out I heard his low voice; well spoken and obviously often used.

'So, I've bought another three companies ... I mean I know I'm kicking on a bit, but ..'

'Eee, you're only fifty-four! But you shouldn't bite off more than you can chew, Fran!' went Lizzie's voice. I was excited – perhaps he was a great businessman who could offer me a job, a position in his great empire ...

I decided to remain incognito. Perhaps he would present himself to me. I went up to the lounge and flicked through the channels, and found the Cricket World Cup on Sky Sports. Pakistan were playing India, and I was delighted to see one of the greats, Sachin Tendulkar, facing one of my heroes, Waqar Younis. I watched Waqar swing the ball in marvellously late at great pace, then run back and swing it the other way to beat the Little Master.

'Great piece of bowlin' that,' remarked Ian Botham from the commentary box. But Tendulkar pasted the following ball to the boundary, and I found myself applauding the two players' genius.

Heavy footsteps approached and Franson came and sat beside me. From the inner pocket of his jacket he took a box of Benson & Hedges and laid it and a gold lighter on the table. The packet had the flags of all the participating World Cup teams around its opening, as they were this year's sponsors. He held out the packet.

'Oh, thanks a lot,' I said, selecting one from the half-empty pack.

'You like cricket, eh?' he said, as if this was something of great significance, and lit our cigarettes with his fancy lighter.

'Thanks. Yes, I always have done. I play a bit at school.'

'Ah ...' he replied mysteriously, as if this were of even greater significance. 'So tell me, what do you want to be when you grow up?'

'I'm not sure. I've thought about business. And then there's law ... But I guess I've always wanted to be a writer, although I know it's difficult to get established.'

'A writer, eh?'

'Yes. What do you do?'

'Oh, I just buy companies, do them up and sell them on for a profit. I've made a lot of money that way, but I've learnt that money isn't everything. Last year I was very ill and spent a few weeks in here, and it made me think about things. And I'm sure the same will have happened to you. I guess your headmaster will call it a character-building experience. What is it, depression?' He leaned forward and spoke quietly, as if he were conducting an important business transaction.

'No, I got spiked with LSD. I'm not sure what's wrong with me yet. I sort of see things that other people can't see.'

'Ah, hallucinations! Yes, I was the same. They'll go away.

170

But you'll always keep that little bit of vision and insight, keep a few steps ahead of the rest. I'm sure you'd make a good businessman. But you have to love money to be good in business.'

We sat in silence for a few moments and I savoured the rare taste of the cigarette. When we'd finished Franson lit another.

'So have you met Branson then?' I asked eagerly, spotting the potential relation, the similarity between the names.

'Richard Branson? I've met him, yes. But we have no business relations. He came and gave a speech at the opening of one of the businesses I'd built up.' His blue eyes sparkled as he recalled something. Wasim Akram bowled a beautiful, swinging yorker only to be no-balled. Franson almost jumped out of his seat. 'What a ball! God, that was very unlucky ... Yes, the perks of money are you can buy whatever you want, obviously. When I was your age, or a little bit older than you, I loved cars ... now I have my favourite car, a Bentley. Five of them, in fact. And a Ferrari, a Lamborghini ... I'm not showing off, I'm just telling you where I get my motivation from. I suppose it's not just cars, it's other things. I know how to spend it, and what it can do for me ...'

Franson talked on for some time, but I felt my concentration slipping once more and sat mesmerized by the cricket, lost in a curiously mixed world of Pakistani fast bowling and cigarette smoke. When he had finished, he rose and I shook his hand, thanking him for the advice and the cigarettes.

'No problem at all, Mr Fountain. I'll be in sooner or later, and maybe if you're better, the nurses will let you take a look at one of my cars.'

'That'd be great. I'll look forward to it.' I imagined our meeting would mark a significant turning point in the career of James Fountain, that I might reach the same age with many millions and remember that this was where it all began.

Later I was sitting in my room watching the news, and Becca brought me my meal, gently smiling as always, but with a bit

171

more of a spring in her step than usual. I commented as much.

'Oh, it's my birthday,' she said, suddenly bubbly with excitement, 'and my boyfriend's taking me to this gorgeous restaurant for a meal!'

'Ah, that's great!' I said, 'happy birthday.'

She smiled her photogenic smile. 'Thanks very much,' she replied, then skipped out of the room. I ate my soup and roast chicken and mashed potato in a jealous gloom, hardly thinking of how the food tasted. Afterwards, I carried the tray back through to her, this time making a point of not smiling, then headed back down the corridor feeling foolish and stupid in my jealousy.

I continued walking past my own room and investigated the other rooms at my end of the corridor. I went into Matthew's room, which was across from my own. I discovered his case and a few things scattered about the room – paperbacks, hairbrush, jeans, a used shirt, mobile phone charger ... But on the whole there was nothing very remarkable to be said for it, and my concentration wavered, this time I felt for good reason. It was important to continually police my thoughts to ensure a progression toward the date of my release.

The room next door was empty, though the one opposite seemed interesting if only for its name, a sign attached to the door reading: The Michael Jackson Room. I concluded from this that the pop king must have set up residence here after some celebrity breakdown or other whilst on tour. Perhaps it was true that he was a little mentally imbalanced as the papers continually alleged. Pushing the door open, I choked on the ensuing dust, and my nose began to bleed. Perhaps it was the shock of discovering the room was full of an unknown person's possessions, the excitement of entering someone else's private world.

It was well lived in. Shelves had been put up to accommodate many books, and I noticed a volume of Shakespeare's complete works, as well as books on psychology including

172

works by Jung and Freud, the philosophers Descartes and Kant. Adorning the walls were posters of U2 and Aerosmith, and strangely enough a small poster of Michael Jackson, from the *Bad* promotion, wearing his leather get-up with a streak of rebellion across his face, as though trying to imitate a youthful Marlon Brando.

A TV and video sat on a little table to my left, and the bed had been made more personalised with a black and red quilt with an elaborate design of roses upon it, giving the room an effeminate feel. Releasing the handkerchief from my nose to find the bleeding had stopped, I breathed carefully and smelt the faint scent of perfume.

Walking back into the corridor, I saw there was only one room remaining to be explored. Situated two doors down from Matthew's room, I remembered seeing Dr Norton and other men in suits, whom I had assumed were doctors, leading people down here. An orange street lamp glow filtered through the half-open shutters of a blind. As I switched on the long ceiling light that reminded me of the kind we had at school, I saw a large, empty table, with a single cushioned wooden chair, its back to the window and two further chairs facing it from the other side. It was evidently a consulting room. A wooden wardrobe like the one in my own room lay to the right, along with a small sink and wall mirror. I opened the wardrobe and found various suit jackets and a couple of smart shirts. In the corner of the room to my right was a typewriter, quite old and ornate, black with silver letters printed on the circular black keys. Part of the mechanism was on display at the top in the old-fashioned style. As its little wooden table had wheels on it, I turned around the chair nearest the window and pulled the typewriter toward me.

There was no paper in the typewriter, but that was of no consequence. This was a communicator. No one in their right mind would use a typewriter rather than a word processor in this day and age. There was a dual purpose to this machine, which only those of higher intelligence could detect. With this machine I could send messages that would reach their destination through spiritual airwaves. Somewhere another machine would receive these communications and create telegrams, which my intended recipients would read. And so I started typing.

BRANSON – HAVE MADE CONTACT WITH YOUR AGENT FRANSON AND AM READY TO BEGIN MY WORK AS BUSINESS APPRENTICE. FEEL THIS COULD LEAD TO AN ABILITY TO TRANSFER MY HIGHER POWERS TO THE WORLD AND HELP IT OUT OF ITS PRESENT CRISIS. EAGERLY AWAIT YOUR REPLY. THE TRANSITION FROM EASTWOOD INTO WESTMORELAND IS AT AN END. THE NEW CASTLE IS UNDER CONSTRUCTION. YOURS SINCERELY JAMES FOUNTAIN.

I sat back and considered that this machine could also be a means of communicating with God. I started afresh, hammering the keys as quickly as my fingers would move.

READY FOR MY NEXT ASSIGNMENT. SO FAR ALL IS GOING WELL. UNDERSTAND THAT MY TIME IN ST LUKE'S WAS INTENDED AS CHARACTER-BUILDING TEST. WHAT IS MY PURPOSE HERE? HAVE RECEIVED VISIT FROM EASTWOOD. IS FRANSON WESTMORELAND? OR NORTON? EAGERLY AWAIT YOUR DIVINE RESPONSE. FROM YOUR SECRET SERVANT ST JAMES.

Suddenly the light went out.
'Hey!' was my automatic response.

'James?' asked Lizzie, as she switched the light back on. 'What are you doing?'

'It's secret. Can't tell you.' Lizzie's surprised eyes fell upon the typewriter.

'So it was you I could hear typing away. But there's no paper in it ...'

'I know.' She folded her arms. 'This is a machine through which I alone can communicate with God. God has placed the machine here for me to transmit information to him.'

'Right. And you believe that do you?' she asked, once more irritating in her knowing and disapproving tone.

'Absolutely. I take it you don't.'

'No, I don't. I think you need another tablet. Come on.'

Relieved to have got the message off in time, and also secretly relieved that Lizzie did not believe me and thus remove my transmitter, I wheeled it back into the corner and put the chair back, following the nurse out.

As we neared the little room where the medication was stored, I feared the messages might not reach their intended destinations if I ingested more medication that would slow my thoughts. It would take the edge off my powers, decrease my effectiveness as an ordained saintly guide. And so, as Lizzie opened the door and selected a bottle, I had already made up my mind.

'I'm not taking it.' I stated boldly.

'Not taking what?'

'That tablet – I refuse to take it.'

'Why? You'll feel better. Your mind'll stop racing.'

'I am better! You're all making this up. Listen – I – am – a – representative – of – God. Was that clear enough for you? AmItalkingtoofastorsomething?!'

'What? The first bit you said was clear, but it made no sense whatsoever.' She spoke slowly and calmly, looking into my eyes with that clear blue-eyed knowingness that made me feel guilty, so that I was compelled to look away. 'The second bit was spoken too quickly. You're going through a bit of a manic phase and I suggest you take this tablet.'

'Manic? Is that what you call my having special God-given powers? Manic! You medical people are so unimaginative! You don't realise that things go on that you can't explain ...'

'I know you're upset that your mother's gone home and you couldn't go with her. I understand that, James.'

'That's got nothing to do with it!'

'Now don't raise your voice, please. There's other patients here and you'll disturb them. Take this tablet.' She held out the circular, button-like object.

'Why?' At that moment a shout came from the lounge. It was Matthew.

'James, do what the nurse says! Do you wanna be in here for the rest of your life?'

I was a little shocked, but took the tablet from Lizzie's open palm, and she sighed with relief. I went into the kitchen, which was empty and clean, Becca no doubt off to her birthday soirée. After drinking down the tablet with ice-cold water I reflected upon the possibility that Matthew could be another agent sent by God to protect and guide me, with troubles to boot to put my own in perspective. After all, my troubles were nothing compared to his. I'd lost Rachel Lockwood, but she was not the love of my life.

In the lounge, I found Robert and Matthew watching *A Few Good Men*. Robert was watching with particular intensity, leaning forward to the screen as Alan had to the Ali fight, turning up the volume at his favourite moments. Matthew had his shoes off and was lying flat on his back on the wooden-framed couch opposite his younger friend. He looked tired and only vaguely interested in the movie, with his head raised and his eyes blank as though they registered the images but could not follow the story-line. He turned his head slowly as I walked in.

'You took that pill then, I hope?' he asked seriously. I

nodded. 'That's good. Sorry to shout by the way, but somebody's gotta talk sense into you. Or else you'll never get out, will you? How long have you been in for now?'

I wasn't sure. Dates meant nothing to me. Nor did any aspect of time. I failed to see why people made such a fuss about it.

'I don't know.'

'You don't know? Then I'll find out.' He got up and sprinted down the corridor, turning right into the office. Soon he was sprinting back, and resumed his position. 'Two weeks, apparently. But not all spent in this hospital, just a few days here.'

'That can't be right!' I exclaimed in astonishment.

'Claire's just checked your notes. And I'm sure they're more accurate than your version of events after what you've been through!'

'I suppose.' It seemed impossible that it had been only two weeks. So two weeks ago I was at school. But what did time mean in this extraordinary world? It could not explain the great depth of things, the secret communication I had just transmitted to God. I still felt time to be of no importance to my mission, in which I now believed with renewed conviction.

I heard banging from the floor above, and it occurred to me I had no idea what was up there. I thought I could hear music, and it was not coming from the television. As I walked down the corridor, the sound became louder.

Reaching the elevator and finding the key missing, I attempted to prise open the doors with my hands. With a great effort I had them open enough for me to sneak through, but I paused for a moment and looked down the shaft, which was at least 5 metres deep. A cold wind blew in my face, and as I stood on the edge I was grabbed from behind and dragged backwards, crying out in shock. The doors slammed shut.

'You stupid bloody kid!' said Claire. 'What did you think you were doing?'

'I thought I could hear a party going on, on the third floor,'

I said, 'There was no key so I thought I might try to climb up there.'

'Ye're a fool. Tha's no party goin' on up there, chuck. An' don't even think about tryin' ta kill yeself. Now get yeself back down an' watch the film!'

17

In the morning Dr Norton came in shortly after I had finished breakfast. I had been up since 4.00 a.m. by Claire's watch, and neither she nor Peter had managed to persuade me to go back to sleep. I had lain for some hours facing my window, waiting for the sun to rise, and the sleeping tablet to wear off. I could think of nothing but the two communications I had sent off, and eagerly awaited their reply.

'How's Mr Fountain today then?' the doctor asked, walking into the room in his workmanlike manner, leaning slightly forward as though he carried a great weight across his shoulders. He sat heavily on the bed.

'Fine! I'm great!'

'Yes ... the nurse says you didn't get a lot of sleep last night. And the notes suggest you've not been well ... are you eating?'

'Oh yes, the food here's lovely!' Nothing could dampen my enthusiasm. I knew things Norton didn't. 'You might think I'm unwell, but God thinks I'm fine and doing a good job. I communicated with him last night by secret transmitter.'

'And what did you say to him?' asked the doctor, seemingly intrigued.

'Ah – now that's top secret. I'd need to know for sure if you're Westmoreland, and the answer may be coming back at some point. But all you need to know is that my work is improving the state of the world ... the future of mankind depends on it.'

'Right ... here's what I'm going to do. I'm going to put you on a higher dose. Now, this will slow you down considerably, but I'm afraid it's absolutely necessary ...' Dr Norton was becoming uncharacteristically animated in his speech. 'I'm sorry. So far we've not been making any progress here. But we will. Now, you're definitely not well. You're over-active, and you're not making much sense. There's no real point in continuing this conversation, I can see this just by looking at you. You are flighty and have delusions of grandeur. Until you start to listen to me, I can do nothing.'

'But ...'

'But nothing. You need to make a serious effort. The nurses have told me everything you've said, and on that evidence a release date is unclear. Search for that insight, no matter how elusive it may be. You are a patient in the psychiatric ward of a hospital. The sooner you get better, the sooner we can get you home.' And then he smacked my knee in that characteristic fashion of his, and away he went, whistling to himself as he walked out of the room.

I pondered these words for some minutes and found them to be false. I knew what I was doing, and God approved – there was nothing more to be concerned about.

With this in mind I drifted quickly out of my room as though blown on a gale, my legs sending me to the lounge as if of their own accord. I found Matthew watching TV, unshaven and tired, in a pale-blue T-shirt and jeans.

'Fancy a game of table tennis?' I asked him, unable to endure the thought of having to sit still and watch television.

'Alright,' he said, rising a little reluctantly from his comfortable position.

The bats were red and green, and I handed the red one to Matthew. Soon we had a rally going but often I would hit the ball too hard and the ball would smack into the wall behind him.

'Take it easy, James! Let's just keep a rally going, shall we?'

'I'm trying. But my powers are so strong right now.'

'What powers?'

'You know what I'm talking about.'

'Then don't talk. Just concentrate on the ball.'

We played on for some time and reached rallies of 30 or so,

until finally Matthew decided he'd had enough and returned to his post in front of the television. I managed to persuade Lizzie to play with me for a while, as well as a new acquaintance, a pretty young nurse in a beige-coloured uniform, named Charlotte. She was a few inches shorter than me, with shoulder-length auburn hair and hazelnut eyes. She had a ready smile and laughed through most of our rallies, as I watched her moving her slim, agile body dexterously around her end of the table. But soon she too tired of playing.

'Eee, I'm out o' puff, James!' she exclaimed in her high-pitched Geordie accent. 'I'll just get me breath back an' then we'll 'ave another game later on, OK?'

'Why aye man, no problem, like.'

'Eee, ye takin' off me Geordie accent, aren't ye! Yer a funny 'un!' she said, laughing as she headed off down the corridor. Matthew was laughing too.

But now boredom had hit, and as it twisted around inside me, I wanted more than anything to be free. I wandered back down the corridor, noticing Robert lying fully clothed on his bed as I walked past his room, snoring loudly on his back with the curtains closed.

Lizzie and Charlotte were not pleased to see me in the office. I sat on one of the chairs watching them going about their everyday work, filing and writing notes, answering the phone.

'Look, if you really think he's that bad you can bring him in and we can check him out. OK? No, Mrs Benson, I can't promise anything ... no. So we'll see you soon, yeah?' Lizzie put down the phone and looked at me. 'James, what are you doin' in here? You know we're busy.'

'I'm bored. I want to get out of here.'

'Well, you know what the answer to that is. Dr Norton says you're not well and that's it. You're not leavin' today. Your mum agrees with me, you should stay in here until you're better. You're not sectioned or anything but that's what the doctor's recommended to us.'

181

'Look, I don't care! I don't care about anything you people say! Let me go home! I've important work to do! The future of the world depends on me! HOW MANY TIMES DO I HAVE TO SAY IT?!'

'Now, James – '

'No, I'm not going to listen to this again. I – am – not – fucking – ill, ok?'

'You're getting aggressive now and if you just – '

'Just what? Just take some more friggin' tablets?!'

'Eh! Stop that language, sunshine!' Charlotte chimed in. 'Ye'll get shot!'

'If you just take some deep breaths an' think about what you're doin' you'd realise you're makin' a big mistake. We're only tryin' to help. That's all,' said Lizzie.

Her eyes were full of care and patience, and watching them remain steady throughout my tantrum had calmed me. I sat somewhat bemused for a moment, wondering where this sudden anger had come from.

'You're bound to be frustrated, but we know you're not right just yet. Now it's time for your next set of tablets and your lunch'll be ready soon. Come on.'

I followed her and took the tablets she handed to me from the little room. The water I took them with cooled my insides, which still seemed alive with anger. But there was some sort of subconscious effort taking place to suppress this anger. I was learning patience as a child learning to walk, taking cautious steps forward, tumbling down, then starting all over again.

However, the perseverance was difficult to sustain, and if I had been a prisoner, fellow inmates would say I was still at the breaking in stage. After lunch, I sat for five painful minutes in front of the TV with Matthew before my limbs began to ache with the constant inactivity of recent weeks. I decided only a bath could be the solution to relax me, and immediately rose and went back to my room to get a towel.

In a bath filled almost to the brim with water and clouds of bubbles, I felt quite dizzy. I had filled the whole thing with hot water and no cold, and my skin burned, the sweat bursting out of my forehead. Just as I felt I was about to pass out I realised I needed to urinate, and, although embarrassed at the idea of going right there in the bathtub, I came up with the idea that my urine could contain healing properties, since I had special powers. And so, I let the stuff come pouring out of me, gaining a strange sense of freedom from turning the bathwater a pale, yellowish green, like a fallen autumn leaf.

But when I eventually got out of the water, I stood up too quickly, felt a sudden and powerful dizziness, and fell immediately to the ground, my head smacking against the floor. When I came to, there was a knocking at the door, and when I opened it naked, thinking nothing of it, there was a scream from Charlotte. She covered her eyes.

'Jesus, I don't look that bad, do I?' I asked. She laughed.

'No, but just get yerself a towel, will ye!' I wrapped the towel around my waist as Charlotte walked suddenly into the bathroom.

'Oh, my God, James! Ye've peed in the bath! That was a silly thing to do wasn't it? Ye'll stink, man! Look, take out that water, wash it out an' put some more in. Ye'll need to have another wash!'

I did as she said, and beneath the fresh bathwater I rubbed the slight lump that had formed on the side of my head from the fall. Perhaps she was right, the peeing in the bath thing was a bit silly. Cheekily, I pulled back the lock on the off chance that she or one of the lovely waitresses would fancy bathing with me. I lay back and imagined taking a bath with Laura, Becca and Charlotte ... and suddenly I was swept into a world where all three were kissing and touching me and each other all over, locked in a blissful and satisfying foursome ...

After this second bath I rose more slowly this time, smirking and thinking how right Charlotte had been to suggest it, but felt the pain throb with renewed vigour at the side of my head.

Back in my room, I combed my hair and sat in the armchair, relaxed and refreshed. My legs began to shake of their own accord, one foot crossed over the other, the black shoes quivering like a bat's wings. And as I sat there immersed in this activity, I observed men in suits leading people backwards and forwards past my room, no doubt down to the consulting room that held my secret transmitter. Time seemed to have speeded up and the people moved to and fro at a gathering pace until their movements became a blur. The shaking of my legs had increased the earth's rotational velocity, moving everything forward. Or was the typewriter some sort of time machine into which I had unwittingly punched a coded message to send time forwards?

Amidst the rapid stream of human traffic, I caught glimpses of faces looking in, people in spectacles both modern and old-fashioned, men with clouds of white hair and younger features, women with large rotund bodies and beautiful faces. It was as if heads had been taken from bodies and transplanted to others. I watched it all whirl past me in a cyclone of confusion, until soon it became too much and I shifted my entranced gaze away from the doorway, and focussed on the garden opposite.

The outside world was carrying on at its normal pace. Evidently time was only moving forwards within the hospital at present, before its transference on a larger scale. In the garden, I perceived with great interest the figure of a man in a heavy, green Barbour jacket with matching waxed hat and black wellingtons, moving about with a shovel between the various borders. He was planting rose bushes in the flower bed furthest from me, sturdy and only half in bloom, with deep red petals and dark green leaves. He had cleared many of the fallen leaves into a large pile in the middle of the lawn. Hurriedly, I took a piece of paper with the sky-blue Nuffield letter heading from the folder beside my bed along with the white ballpoint provided. I then wheeled the table towards me, and began to write.

184

RED ROSEBUSHES = SYMBOLS OF GOODWILL
TO SAINT JAMES
HALF IN BLOOM = SIGN OF GOODWILL TO
COME
CLEARED PILES OF LEAVES = CLEARING AWAY
THE WORLD'S EVIL
WORLD STILL MOVING TOWARDS FINAL
CONCLUSION
EAST STILL MOVING INTO WEST
TIME IS HEALING EVERYTHING
LIFE WILL NEVER BE THE SAME ⑦

I stopped writing, but realised the ideas were not flowing as they once had. The ideas came slowly, and, it seemed, against the grain of my natural inclination. I sat in some confusion, wondering why it had taken me so long to get the ideas on to paper. And there had been so much more that I had been unable to articulate. Something was stopping me from spreading my wings. Something was clipping them. Some*one*.

I marched through to the nurses' office, and burst through the closed door.

'What do you think this is, EH!' I shouted, angry and shaking all over.

'What do I think what is?' asked Lizzie, standing up from her chair and looking wide-eyed across her desk at a young girl. 'Can't you see I'm busy?'

'No, I don't give a shit about that anyway! You just tell me why you're giving me all this –' I'd lost the word. Everything was slower, and I wanted to sleep. I felt myself fighting it off.

'Medication?' suggested Lizzie.

'Yeah! I'm not taking it anymore. You – people – are … trying to stop me!'

'No, we're trying to make you better, James.' She fixed me with her blue eyes.

'But you can't explain this – time is moving forwards! The

people have been moving past my door at great speed! And that's because of my power. And you're CRUSHING it!' I grabbed some papers from the desk and flung them to the floor, and in a flash Lizzie had grabbed me by the shoulders and bustled me out of the office, motioning for the girl to remain seated. I noticed she had short reddish-brown hair and a pale, clear complexion, and wore flared blue jeans and a long, green coat, which she had not taken off. She reminded me of the students I had seen struggling against the wind.

'Go into your room and think about what you've done. This is not you. You're a nice young lad normally. Have a lie down if you feel tired. You'll feel better for it, I promise.' I listened to her smooth voice, calm and hypnotic in my present condition. My vision was cloudy now and I knew this was not due to some mark on my spectacles. I needed rest.

So I did as Lizzie said, and as I went back to my room, took off my glasses and got half-naked into bed, the heat of the anger left my cheeks and the tightness across the cheekbones receded. Suddenly nothing mattered anymore, and as I lay on my side I gazed at the blurred fuzz of light-grey clouds and wondered if it might rain, then slowly fell asleep.

18

Four days passed. I received no reply from my communications to God and Richard Branson, but after some investigations learned that the girl I had seen in the office talking to Lizzie was in fact a patient at the Nuffield, and had been for some weeks. She told me her name was Cathy, and that she had returned after a trip home to see her family for a week. I sat in the lounge with her, drinking tea.

'What was it like going home?' I asked her.

'Oh, you know, strange. I feel like I've been in here forever. And I miss my friends from Durham. I'm studying English Language at the university there.' She spoke very clearly and correctly, choosing her words carefully. Her large brown eyes always looked into my own as she spoke, seeming to hold closely-guarded secrets. 'What do you do?'

'Oh, I'm still at school.'

She looked surprised. 'Really? How old are you?'

'Sixteen. I'm in the final year of my GCSEs.'

'I thought you were older. You remind me of someone I know – one of my mates from uni called Tom. Where are you from?'

'Hartlepool, though I can barely remember it now.'

'I know. You go sort of brain-dead just sitting all the time, doing the same things. Do you play table tennis?'

'Yes! Fancy a game?'

'Oh, I'd love one. We'll just play rallies though, yeah?'

We reached a highest rally of 60, at which point Cathy said she was tired and wanted to rest.

'We'll play again soon though, James, yeah? Come and see me sometime. Mine's the room next to yours, the Michael Jackson room or something.'

'Cool – see you later. And have a nice rest!' I watched her smile and walk back to her room, her tight purple and black top emphasising her slim figure, her movements graceful and unhurried. I heard a laugh behind me, and turned to see Robert and Matthew observing from the far corner, Robert smoking another Dunhill.

'Have you met the love of your life then, James? "Shall I compare thee to a summer's day?" ' joked Matthew. Robert laughed.

'You should ask her out!' he said through his laughter.

'Very funny, guys. I'll have to check with the nurse first though!'

I went and sat with them. To my disappointment I learned they had each been given release dates, and subsequently decided to discharge themselves.

'Yeah, I think I'm ready to get back to work now. Those tablets really do work if you let them, James,' said Matthew. 'Your problem's that you don't know you're ill.'

'Right ...' It had become a dull topic to me, this illness thing. 'So when do you leave?'

'Well, I'm givin' Robert a lift home on Tuesday the twenty-seventh – two days' time. And then I'll drive back to Durham. You'll get better twice as fast without us here.'

I stole one of Robert's cigarettes, taking it slowly out of the classy red and gold box, and lit it. This time Matthew made no moves to stop me.

'And you can learn to stop that before you get out as well,' he said. 'How long have you been smoking?' I blew out a line of smoke towards the ceiling.

'Since I got here.'

'Oh, man, you don't want to start in 'ere. Don't let it get to you,' suggested Robert, speaking with the hint of a London accent.

'I just get bored, that's all. Who knows, I might never get out.'

'Ah, you will,' said Matthew, slowly rocking his head with a serious expression on his face.

'And we'll come and visit you, won't we, Rob?' Robert looked at me and nodded through his usual cloud of pale-blue smoke.

Soon I drifted back to my room, the familiar afternoon tiredness creeping up on me once more. I had taken to having two-hour naps to help shrug it off, along with the tedium. Around two o'clock I heard Matthew and Robert laughing near the lift, then going off for their usual couple of pints in a pub somewhere, leaving me irritated and jealous before falling into an embittered sleep.

I awoke to the sound of my mother's voice, and for a couple of seconds before I opened my eyes, I thought I was at home and being woken up to catch the bus to school. But as I opened them I realised with disappointment where I was, that it was late afternoon, the sky dark-blue over the Jesmond rooftops, and that my mother was standing over me.

'James! James! We're all here, darling! We thought you might like to have a walk across the road for a cup of hot chocolate.' I turned and saw her attempting to be bright and cheerful, and my disappointment melted.

'Oh, great!' I said, suddenly conscious in my sleep/wake state that once more I would breathe fresh air, or at least as fresh as the city of Newcastle had to offer. I would be part of the real world for a change.

As I dressed, my father walked in with my sister, who went about tidying up the *Guardian* newspapers, which had accumulated on the floor around the bed.

'What are you reading the *Guardian* for?' my father asked, a die-hard Tory. I imagined he was worried I was about to become a socialist as well as a maniac.

'It's for the Arts section. I like reading the book reviews, OK? The *Guardian* have the best people at the moment.'

'Shut up, Chris! Leave him alone.' said my mother, springing to my defence. 'Oh, they change the bed for you every day, do they?' she said, examining the crisp, clean sheets. 'That's nice of them.'

My sister took the tape out of my Walkman. 'There's only one tape here! Do you listen to the same tape over and over again? *The Love Album*!'

'Yes, I like it, alright?' The sudden invasion of privacy annoyed me, but nevertheless the family ruminations were a welcome distraction. My knees clicked noisily as I put on my shoes, making a sound like two stones being bashed together.

'What's that?' my mother asked.

'The doctor told me it's the Chlorpromazine medication. It gets in the joints.'

'Ooh, does it hurt?'

'Not really.'

'Well anyway, you probably won't have to take those tablets for much longer. The nurses say you've improved a lot. OK then, shall we get moving?'

My mother turned the key in the lift and within moments I was out, swinging back the door and stepping out into a cool early evening breeze. We walked around the back of the hospital between some concrete bollards, and I looked up at the black silhouettes of trees and watched them waving at the dying day and greeting the oncoming night, deep pink floating on the horizon as the stars came out. I suppressed an impulse to shout out loud as we entered the high street and moved along past the little shops, an antique dealers with a handsome French dresser shining from behind protective wire mesh, oil paintings glowing in approval from golden frames through the window of an art dealers. I watched people go in and out of the newsagents across the street, cars swishing to and fro as if nothing remarkable had ever taken place.

We crossed the road at the traffic-lights. I looked up at the lounge window from which I would normally peer out in jealousy at the passing pedestrians and traffic, and felt wonderfully grateful that I was now part of it all, at least for an hour or so.

In a few minutes we came to Jimmy's coffee shop, painted dark green around large windows with gold lettering along the top. As we went inside, the busy atmosphere was stimulating, waitresses buzzing around with trays, and people sat in various groups on both the raised and lower levels. I listened to the fragments of chit-chat and laughter, men talking about future business transactions, one woman muttering close by to a friend about how she'd love to divorce her husband were it not for the children. And as I gazed upon this microcosm of human life before me, I felt a strange disconnection from it. That I was no longer fully part of it only served to increase my fascination for it, as if observing a rare species in its natural habitat.

'What would you like, James?' asked my mother, tapping me on the shoulder.

'Oh ...' I looked up at the ornately-written chalkboard above the counter. 'A large hot chocolate, please.'

At a circular black and white table made of imitation marble, we sat together and drank.

'People used to call grandpa Jimmy, didn't they, Daddy?' I asked.

'Yes, they did. Or Jim,' my father replied.

'Maybe he set this coffee shop up and ran it on the side, and when he died the new owners named it after him.'

'Oh, I don't think so. He was too busy consulting and teaching at the university,' my mother interjected.

'Anyway, stop talking rubbish!' exclaimed my sister, raising her gothic lashes in schoolgirlish scorn.

'Victoria, stop that!' my mother whispered, trying to dampen her antagonism and prevent a scene.

'Have you been watching any of the cricket?' my father asked, using the opportunity to get a word in.

'Some. I saw a bit of the Pakistan–India game. Waqar

bowled well, swung it both ways. And Tendulkar was pretty amazing.'

'Yes. He got a hundred, didn't he? And he was the man of the match. Good game. I saw the highlights when I got back from work.'

I sipped my hot chocolate and added a little more sugar, engrossed by the spectacle of normal human life. As I sat facing the whole room from the corner, I watched students coming in for takeaway coffees, ordering mocha and cappuccinos and sprinkling cinnamon; an old lady taking her cup across to a small, empty table by the window. She caught my eye and I watched her looking across at me through neat little glasses. Her hair was white and curly and she was immaculately dressed, taking off her large cream coat and laying it across the empty seat opposite. She seemed quite content to sit in solitude, warming her hands on the coffee cup. I wondered what the occasion was, whether it was her birthday or wedding anniversary. Or perhaps she always dressed like that, in a dark-blue suit with a long skirt and cream blouse, hoping to meet someone new to help her forget her lost love. Perhaps a solution to the mystery was lodged within the intricate gold brooch she wore on the lapel of her jacket. Perhaps she was waiting to meet the person who had given this to her, in life or in death.

To her right were the businessmen, dressed in expensive suits and still talking loudly of impending transactions, seemingly unable to relax despite the fact it was Sunday. A man to their left sat alone at a table working his way through the various sections of a Sunday broadsheet.

'You like to watch people, don't you, James?' my mother asked, catching me staring at the man with the papers. 'You like to observe.'

'I suppose. People are interesting – we all want different things, don't we? I mean, to me, talking business on a Sunday's crazy. But to those guys over there it's great fun.'

'Yes, but some businessmen in the City work on a Sunday, James. I've got clients that do. Anyway, they have to talk about it or else nothing would get done,' my father said.

'Alright, but that's not my point. What I'm saying is these people love to talk about work. Others prefer to read the papers or talk to mates. And that poor old lady in the corner looks quite content to be alone with her coffee. She might not be, of course, but again she's different. That's what I like about this place – there's an interesting mix of people. By the way, I had a meeting with a businessman named Franson a few days ago. He said he'd met Branson, and so I sent Branson a message.'

'Richard Branson? How did you do that?'

'Ah, that's a secret. I've got a secret machine.'

I sat in the ensuing silence and finished the hot chocolate. My mother glanced at my father and they rose. Victoria was still staring at me, with eyes that looked as though they had been beaten around the edges. Her thick eyeshadow and eyeliner made her look like an abused child of 13, the opposite of the pampered care we'd both received all our lives.

We returned to the hospital through the orange haze of the streetlights, a fog having spread its way along the high street and the surrounding area. My father and sister each hugged me, and my mother took me back up to the ward. I was not reluctant to go back. I had tasted hope, and expected to taste more.

'Hi, Lizzie! Yes, he was good, weren't you?' She spoke as if she were talking about my little cousin Richard, or our Yorkshire Terriers.

I went back to my room in embarrassment, hearing her voice drop to a whisper as I paused at the threshold. Evidently not that good, then, I thought.

But the next morning Charlotte took me for a walk to Jesmond Dene. The morning was fine and crisp with clouds high and thin in the blue, the sun blinding from its position low in the sky. A slight frost encrusted the pavement. *En route* to the dene we passed Jesmond Cricket Club, and I remembered charity matches between star-studded World XIs and England XIs which had been held there recently, sponsored by a distant uncle. My mother and father had attended, a signed programme of which I had framed and hung in a space on my bedroom wall. Malcolm Marshall had played one of the games, and I was saddened to remember an article saying he was dying of cancer.

'Do you play much cricket yourself then, James?' asked Charlotte, in response to my long monologue about the cricket matches.

'Yes, I play for my school and Hartlepool Cricket Club junior team. I've missed the nets this year though, being stuck here.'

'Ah, ye'll soon get back in the swing of it! What a beautiful day!'

I looked at her gently smiling face and could feel nothing but gratitude for this sudden increase in freedom I had been allowed. I reflected that there had been times when I'd thought I would never see daylight again, longed to feel the ice-cool breeze on my face. And remembering this served to heighten the bliss of being allowed to go out, to feel part of it all once more.

The streets were quiet as we walked through the affluent housing estate, an occasional car humming past. I checked the numberplates of parked cars and told Charlotte whenever I spotted one I felt to be of significance. On one occasion I saw one that ended YCN, which I remembered from a past brainstorm was short for: You Can Now. I kept this one to myself, wary of divulging too much of my secret knowledge. The numberplate symbolised that I was on the right track to freedom.

The dene was a revelation to me. There we passed snowdrops and daffodils which had spread between tall oaks and beeches, sycamores releasing their seeds and spiralling down like tiny helicopter propellers. I shouted out with excitement when I saw a rare red squirrel moving furtively about, and I explained to Charlotte what the various different birds were that we saw and heard. Pied wagtails leapt to and fro as though they were playing some game and not frantically looking for food, and as we crossed the wide old bridge I caught the surreal turquoise and orange of a kingfisher perched on the bank of the stream, scanning the water for rising fish.

The sky was alive with bird-song, nature rejoicing at spring's commencement, and I listened in wonder to Charlotte's proclamation that all of this was man-made, that not a single stick existed until then. We paused at the bridge on the way back and as I leaned over the edge and looked down, I thought of what a genius this man must have been, to have created something so serene from what was originally just a field.

As we began to walk back I stopped at an artist's little stall. He had a bushy grey beard and was sat on a small stool painting very slowly with watercolours. As I looked at the paintings on sale I thought he captured the park beautifully, imagined the hours of craft that he put in, selling his work at a remarkably cheap price. I watched him utterly engrossed, and realised he had found something far greater than monetary gain could ever bring him.

On returning to the hospital ward, I thanked Charlotte for the walk and decided to take a nap, having not slept so well the previous night. I awoke around lunchtime and walked down to the lounge and spoke with the cleaners Pat and Betsy. Pat was ruing her granddaughter's choice of boyfriend. Linda came over and took my order for lunch, spotting the cigarette in my hand and shaking her head.

After the cleaners had gone back to finish their work, Linda brought me a plate of ham sandwiches. I ate them contemplatively, looking out upon the high street and remembering

Jimmy's coffee shop, watching people going about their daily business, taking note of the patterns of colours of the cars. But there were no strict patterns any more, and I saw no number-plates whose messages I was able to decode.

Suddenly I heard a familiar voice coming from behind me.

'Hi, James, how are you, like?' I turned and saw my friend Ian Lefting standing in the doorway dressed in his school blazer and tie, smiling. 'Surprise, surprise! How are you?'

'Ian! I'm not too bad, man, how are you?'

'Oh, not bad. I've been worried about you, though, so I phoned your mum and asked if I could visit. I'm missin' Games but I don't really care.' I noticed he'd had his dark hair cut short and gelled forward like his hero Keith Gillespie.

'I noticed Newcastle are doing well.'

'Aye! Keegan's got us scorin' loads o' goals. Defence isn't too sharp, like, but ye can't have everything! We're playin' Man U on Wednesday. My friend's got tickets, the lucky bastard ... Oh, an' there's another surprise!'

Suddenly his younger sister Susan came in, only a year younger and all flowing blonde hair and shining, intelligent blue eyes. I'd had a crush on her a couple of years before, and to me she was still the definition of an angel.

'Susan!'

'Oh, James, we've been so worried about you, man. How are you? You look well!' she said, hugging me gently and close.

'I'm OK.'

'Let's go and have a sit down,' she said.

I took them down to my room, and Ian and Susan went about looking at all the cards on the wall, which had grown considerably in number in recent days. There was almost no space left on the wall. I sat in the armchair feeling older than my friends, but honoured to be getting so much attention and affection. Susan came over and gave me a kiss on the cheek and hugged me, and for once Ian showed no irritation. I remembered visiting his house near Morpeth and how I would

196

always sneak into her room when he went to the toilet and snatch a couple of seconds chatter with Susan and then sneak back out again. And how I'd sent her a Valentine's card as a fourteen-year-old and got nothing from her, knowing that she must have recognised my writing. And our stilted conversations in the aftermath. How I'd tried to heal everything by sending her a Penguin 60 containing seven of James Herriot's short stories. She had always aspired to becoming a vet, shutting herself up in her room and working constantly at her GCSE Maths, Biology, Physics and Chemistry.

'Thanks for the lovely letter you wrote me Susan. I'm sorry you cried.'

'Oh, that's alright. I cried all day long when I heard, it was so sad ... But that book you gave me helped. I read it and thought of you. I know you're tough and you'll make it through this. Look at all these cards ... everybody cares about you.'

'Yeah, man,' said Ian, 'you've gotta get yeself outta here. An' then we can play rugby and cricket again at my house! An' there's some great parties comin' up!'

From a white polythene bag he produced a football magazine and pointed out an article about Newcastle that he thought I might be interested in.

'Hey, I'm a Leeds fan, you know!' I said, laughing.

'Aye, but tha's always room for one more in the Toon Army, like!'

Soon their time was up, and they needed to catch the train home. I watched them head to the lift from my doorway, and witnessed the distressing sight of Susan beginning to cry uncontrollably, reminding me of the time her dog had died and I'd been drawn into her depression. Ian put his left arm around her shoulders, waving with his right and trying to smile as she sobbed, the lift doors closing in front of them like curtains at the end of an opera.

19

Wednesday came, and I realised Matthew and Robert had gone. The ward seemed very quiet without them, and I missed our late night conversations and the reassurance that they were always there if I needed cheering up.

After breakfast, I sat with Pat, Betsy and Laura, smoking another of Pat's cigarettes and feeling guilty that I'd cadged so many without giving any back. Laura seemed to have been given a temporary reprieve regarding her lazy boyfriend, and the conversation had now turned to the news that a notorious patient had returned to the ward after a year of absence.

'Tom 'arris? Eee, he'll give 'em no end of grief!' said Pat, ''e's a rascal, 'e is.'

'Eee, an d'ya remember when 'e used to walk around with na clothes on? All over the place an' all!' lamented Betsy.

'Aye, an' 'e tried to touch me once,' said Laura, 'said I was 'is little blonde bombshell!'

At this the two older women cracked into laughter, Laura momentarily fighting off the urge to laugh herself and then giving up.

'Eee, these southerners ... Reet, better get movin' I suppose,' said Pat. I got up with them and went back down the corridor. As I did so, I examined all the rooms. Robert's old room was now empty. The old lady was still sat gazing through the window from her chair, though her head turned towards me as I walked past. But as I reached my own room I looked across and found a balding man lying in bed, in the room next door to Matthew's old one, taking deep drags on a cigarette.

I walked into his room. The man turned his head to reveal a neatly trimmed dark beard, which matched the small amount of closely trimmed hair around his scalp. His arms and shoulders were bare, so I guessed he must be naked as Pat had said he was before. How bizarre to walk around naked all the time. Maybe he'd been to one of those holiday resorts where that was the done thing.

''allo, there,' he said, in a cockney accent, 'what's your name, then?'

'James Fountain.'

'Tom 'arris,' he said, holding out his hand. I shook it, and he offered me a Silk Cut. He lit a new one off his old one. 'Pleased to meet you. 'Ave a seat.' I sat in the armchair. 'So what do you do then?' he asked, sitting up straight to reveal his puny upper body. He looked to be quite tall.

'I'm supposed to be at school. But I got spiked with LSD and now I'm in here.'

'Fuckin' 'ell, LSD? Fuckin' jokers. At a party was it?'

'Yes. I thought everyone had made it up, but bits of the night have slowly come back to me so that now I believe them.'

'Right, yeah, must be a bit strange that. I mean I just 'ad a massive breakdown. I'm a scriptwriter for TV an' I was workin' long hours. And then suddenly – ' he clicked his fingers, ''appened just like that.' He took a long drag on his cigarette and gazed into space, then cleared his throat and ran a hand across his beard.

'But you're OK now?' I asked.

'Well, no, I come 'ere last night 'cos I was frightened of a relapse. But I think everything's OK. Just stayin' for a couple o' days rest. That's what it's all about, man, gettin' enough rest.' His dark brown eyes were glazed and tired. Suddenly they regained some of their shine. 'Ever seen *The Fast Show* before?' I nodded. 'Ah, that's the kind of stuff I've been tryin' to write with my mate for this new series we've got planned, 's all in the case.' He indicated a thin, black Delsey briefcase with a red plastic stripe down the middle.

'Cool. I like *The Fast Show*.'

'Great, innit? Do you like *Trivial Pursuit*?'

'Yes, haven't played it much recently though.'

'Well, I think they've got a board here. If you give me a half hour, I'll get showered and see you down in the lounge for a game. 'ow's that sound?'

'Great, I'll see you down there. Cheers for the fag.'

'Oh, forget it, mate.'

I went back to my room and read the paper. There were more disagreements amongst the Tories amid Labour's inexorable rise. Bored with the articles about NHS waiting lists and petty politics, I flicked through to the Arts section, and an interview with Sean Penn, who was publicising his new film, *Dead Man Walking*.

Half an hour later, and I was in the lounge waiting for Tom. I looked down the corridor and saw him walking back to his room with a towel wrapped around his waist, Lizzie getting annoyed with him and telling him to get dressed. He laughed loudly and treaded slowly on his way, unfazed by the criticism and shrieks of disgust his semi-nakedness provoked.

I found the board and set it up, and then Tom came in, clothed but barefoot.

'Oh, so you found the board then? Nice one. Pick a colour.'

The game lasted for some time, and when we both had six pieces of pie there was a titanic struggle over the final questions, mainly because neither of us seemed to know much general knowledge after all. Eventually Tom's patience ran out.

'Let's call it a draw, eh, mate?' he suggested. 'I'm startin' to get edgy!'

'OK, cheers, man. Good game.'

'Hey, you pushed me all the way there!' He shook my hand in a vice-like grip.

As I began to pack the board away, Tom walked off and Lizzie came up the corridor.

''Ello, James! You did well there, didn't ye? Most of us can't sit still with 'im for that long. A whole hour! Your concentration's definitely comin' back. You'll be home before you know

200

it. Here's your tablets and some milk. I know you prefer to take them with milk.'

'Thanks.'

'I hear you went out for a walk with Charlotte yesterday. It's lovely down the dene isn't it?'

'Oh, beautiful. I love the way it's laid out, with that big bridge across it and the stream between all those enormous trees. The stream attracts lots of different birds – I even saw a kingfisher. And there was an interesting old artist there too. I might buy one of his paintings next time I go.'

'And you'll have to get your mum to take you into some of the little shops round Jesmond. They're quite nice too. She told me she's coming up today when I spoke to her on the phone earlier. See you later on.'

She walked back down the corridor, and I got up and pushed the table tennis table against the wall and hit the ball back and forth to myself, seeing if I could create a never-ending rally. After I had tired of this, I walked back to my room. When I glanced across at Tom's room I saw through the half-open door that he was graced by the presence of his girlfriend or wife, a young woman of about 25. She had long, wavy ginger hair and was half-naked, her large breasts bulging in her bra, her slim waist pushed up against his as they kissed. Her beautiful head rocked back and her eyes closed as he kissed her delicately on the neck.

Sulkily, I trudged into my room and sat in the chair, once again picking up the paper, but then with a sudden impulse threw it to the floor. I pulled Rachel's card off the wall and sat looking down at it, not sure exactly what I was looking for. But I was jealous, and I knew it. That bastard Giles, I thought. There was nothing to be done, nothing to be said. As I looked out of the window at the green leafless lawn, I thought of all the people who had once warned me that this is what happened to everyone when they were 16. How wrong I was to think it would never happen to me. I decided I could never

201

meet a girl – my chance had passed. I had been left on the sexual scrapheap, at the boundary between childhood and adulthood. How could I get anyone to take me seriously living in a place like this?

Later that day my mother arrived. By then I was in a better mood, my jealousy having somehow evaporated in the midst of a lot of reading of the other supportive cards on the wall. When my mother came in I was still standing reading them.

'Hi, James! Look who I've brought to see you!'

Two little mouths were around my ankles and I saw that they belonged to our two Yorkshire Terriers, Sooty and Sweep. I smiled and bent down to stroke their little smiling faces, both barely a year old and not more than a foot in length, though Sooty was the largest.

'They want to go for a walk, don't you? Shall we walk over to Jesmond Dene, then? Charlotte said you like it there.'

'Yes, that'd be great. It's lovely there.'

We set off into the late afternoon, a gorgeous dampness lingering in the air after a half hour of recently fallen rain. But it was cold, and I pulled the scarf tighter around my neck to keep warm.

On our return, I found Tom standing by the lift kissing his girl goodbye, and after a quick cup of tea in the lounge, my mother was saying goodbye to me. I was angry all of a sudden when she began walking down to the lift.

'You're leaving me here to rot,' I said to her, after she hugged me and kissed me on the forehead.

'No, darling, of course I'm not! I love you so much. And you'll be able to go home soon, I'm sure.' I saw she was upset as the lift doors closed, and I was sorry I had used such a thoughtless tone with her.

Tom told me that Newcastle were playing Manchester United later that night, so after dinner I went up to the lounge. Through the rear windows I saw two or three tall metal poles with red lights at the top of them, shining through the darkness. They were keeping me here, and the red lights were something to do with surveillance. Nothing had changed, and nor did they appear to want it to. The red lights represented the danger that I faced, hemmed in with nowhere to go.

'What are ye doin', James?' I jumped at the sudden interruption of Lizzie's voice.

'Oh, I'm just admiring your surveillance techniques.'

'Surveillance?'

'Those red lights. I know what they're for. You're watching me all the time, making sure I never go home.'

'I think you're being inappropriate again, James. Those lights are nothin' to do with this hospital.'

'I don't believe you. You're covering something up.' I spoke slowly and quietly.

'I'll get some more meds. I think you need them.'

'No! No more meds . . . I know what you're doing here!' But she had gone.

By the time she returned I had regained my composure, despite a lingering concern that those lights held a greater significance than I was being led to believe. I took the tablets and sat waiting for the game to start. I had to keep my cool.

'Now let's not have any more paranoid talk. You know we care about you here. You're perfectly safe, OK?' said Lizzie. There was something reassuring in her voice, which made me believe her, no matter how much I did not want to.

'I suppose. I'm sorry.'

'Ah, don't worry,' she said, as she walked away.

I played a game of table tennis with Cathy, who now had a new haircut, slightly shorter and dyed auburn like her mother. She was sleekly dressed in tight black nylon trousers and a velvet black polo neck. We sat to have a chat before the game started.

'Ah, that was good! Table tennis is cool,' she reflected, smiling and curling a piece of her hair around her right index finger. 'I might be going home in the next week or so. They reckon they're a lot happier with me now. And one of my professors from Durham visited me today to plan how I can catch up on the work.' My heart sank. Tom would be leaving soon, and I would be alone.

'Excellent! I'm really pleased for you. I wish we'd had a chance to get to know each other better,' I said, trying to be cheerful.

'Oh, I'll give you my address and everything, so we can keep in touch! You seem like a really nice guy.'

Peter and Tom came in suddenly.

'Newcastle! Ow-ay the lads!' cried Peter.

'Eh, mate, I'm a Man U fan, 'ave a bit o' respect!' said Tom, who was still barefoot but now had a Red Devils scarf around his neck.

'Football ...' sighed Cathy, 'right, I'm off to listen to some music. Take care, James. And you two – don't make fun of him, OK?'

'Eh, what ye sayin' like? Wa only watchin' the game!' exclaimed Peter.

'See you later, James,' she said softly, smiling modestly before walking slowly back down the corridor. Peter shot a friendly glance at me.

'Woah, looks like yer on a winner there, son! Looks like ye've scored before the game's started!'

'Ha, ha. We're just friends, alright? And she's leaving soon.'

'Ah, never mind, son. Ye win some ye lose some. Ah but you're a Leeds fan, aren't ye? Which means ye lose some and then ye lose some more! Ha, ha, ha!'

'Pete, man, where's the beers? I thought it was your turn to get 'em in!' said Tom.

'You must be jokin'!' said Pete dryly, displaying his wolfish grin.

The first half was exciting, Manchester United's passing adventurous and precise, Newcastle coming back from one–nil down through a great header by Alan Shearer at the far post.

But even though the game was so interestingly poised at half-time, a tiredness had enveloped me. With my eyelids pulling themselves down like broken window blinds, I got up.

'I can't watch anymore, I'm too tired,' I said.

'Ah, you pussy! Watch the rest o' the game with the lads!' said Tom.

'Come on, man, I'm tired!'

'Oh, alright then. But you're still a pussy goin' to bed at this time!'

'Night, James,' said Peter. I could hear Tom's laughter echoing down the corridor even when I reached my room.

After washing, I climbed into bed, and listened to the faint murmur of music coming through the walls from Cathy's room, like secret messages that only I could hear.

Tom left the very next day, saying that he felt 'top dollar' again, and hoped that eventually I would too. The three days that passed were almost identical, walks to Jesmond Dene, visits from my mother, table tennis, conversations with Cathy … And then came the greatest moment of my life.

Dr Norton came into my room and sat, as he had done every morning for the past 17 days. Even his choice of suit did not vary much.

'How do you feel?'

'OK. A little bored, but OK.'

'Sleeping alright?'

'Yes. The nurse Lizzie reckons I sleep too much.'

'I know – that's why I think you should go home for the night. Give you a bit of a break. What do you think?'

'Really? Am I really allowed to go home?!'

'Yes – but don't get too excited. If all goes well, we can plan a longer trip for you soon after, but until then we need to be careful. I'm still not sure about the meds you're on, they don't work forever on all people … but we'll see. Give your parents a ring to let them know they can pick you up.' And then he slapped my leg and walked from the room. I slapped my hands together in pure happiness, and reached for the telephone.

My father arrived an hour later. With my overnight bag across my shoulder, I waved to the secretary, and to Lizzie, Charlotte, and Cathy, who was peering shyly from her doorway. She came running up suddenly with a slip of paper in one of her delicate hands.

'James, I'm leaving tomorrow morning, so I'll give you this now. It's got my address and phone number for my flat at Durham. Good luck, and I promise I'll write soon!'

'Oh, thanks, Cathy. Best of luck to you too!' I was sad she was leaving, and hugged her suddenly.

When I got in the front seat of the car and strapped myself in, it occurred to me that I was truly going back, and I felt afraid. As my father steered the car along Osborne Road, out of Jesmond and towards the city, it felt as though the whole world was watching me through the car windows. As we stopped at traffic-lights by the cathedral, it seemed shoppers were looking in on me, at the alien visitor, the prisoner, the victim.

A mist above the motorway made me feel vaguely uneasy. I realised I still had a partial belief in the vision I had seen of Eastwood blending into Westmoreland. After all, I recognized none of the roads. And there was so much greenery that was not there previously.

'They've changed all of this area, haven't they? Knocked down a few houses and factories?' I asked my father.

'No – it's been the same for ages. I drive up here every month to go to meetings.'

I decided to stop talking. My father's tone told me he was irritated by my inquiry. But I could not believe it. There was nothing familiar about this road, and I knew there should be. The A19 to Newcastle was by no means alien to me.

As we turned into Elwick, it felt like a great mystery had begun to unravel. We drove past a street to our right, where I remembered Gaby Antrim lived. But as we entered the heart of

206

the village, the little whitewashed houses, The McOrville, The Spotted Cow and the village green with its ornate little wishing well, all seemed only vaguely familiar.

Through the slight mist I studied a house at which I was sure another girl I knew lived. I remembered the guys from the pub, John, Ruud, Jack and the rest. In fact Jack had come staggering out after his usual pre-Sunday lunch skinful, moving his short, stout frame back up to Elwick Hall, a cigarette in the corner of his mouth.

'There's Jack!' my father said, catching sight of him in the rear-view mirror. 'Looks like he's just been for a pint.'

The hills rolled out in front of us, and the memory of the area became less vague. But as I tried to picture our house and street in the midst of the farmland rolling towards us, the images would still not come, and all I could remember were the fronts of various detached homes, and I could not be sure which was our own. Finally, we turned and drove up the dark tree-lined bank that took us past my old primary school, and round the corner.

'Oh, right!' I exclaimed as my father drove round a small coppice and parked the car on the drive of a house. As I got out of the car and looked up at it, I realised I still did not recognize it. But I knew I was supposed to, and indeed I wanted to. It seemed this was the final piece of the puzzle. But the fact was that the brown garage door, the dark bricks and the white plastic intersections of the double-glazed windows seemed completely unfamiliar. As I walked up the pathway, my father took my bag and I walked slowly across the lawn to examine a remarkable dome-shaped tree, its leaves just beginning to come into bud.

As I opened the door, my mother leapt out from nowhere and grabbed me, hugging me and crying joyously.

'Oh, James, it's so good to have you home!'

'OK, OK. Thanks.' Sooty and Sweep were at my feet, little bundles of energy, yapping and giving me their little smiles, and I bent down to stroke them.

'Go into the lounge and get yourself comfortable. The fire's on,' she said as she walked off into a room with beige Formica surfaces, which I guessed was the kitchen.

I examined myself for a moment in the large, mahogany-framed mirror. My thick hair was combed at the centre into long curtains that went past my ears, my eyes peering large and darkly bemused through glasses.

'Go into the lounge, then,' said my father, 'your mother's just putting the kettle on.'

I took a deep breath and stepped to my right onto pale green carpet into a spacious room with a wooden-topped fireplace cut into a cracked-stone flue, above which was a dramatic view of the bleak, windswept moors of Haworth painted with oils. This arrested my attention for some minutes as I lost myself in the scene. I sat in a corner by one of the two large black wooden speakers and took my shoes off, lifting my feet slowly on to a cubic pouffe, Sooty jumping up to pant close to my face before lying across my legs. My father opened a dark wooden cabinet in the far corner to reveal a black stereo, and turned some acoustic Eric Clapton on low.

'So, James,' he said finally, 'you glad to be back?' I considered his question. Was I less terrified now that I had got through the door of a house that I was supposed to recognize? Or more so, now that I realised my worst fears were now reality?

'Yes, I'm pleased. It's nice to be back,' I said.

My father opened a newspaper and began to read. I laid my head back. I had to suppress a desire to go roaming into every corner of the house until I had created a new memory of it. I wanted everything to appear as though it were normal, not to arouse suspicion that I had a memory disorder and would have to spend more time in hospital while it was somehow corrected. But only then would I be glad to be back, when I had re-familiarized myself.

My mother brought in the tea tray. I listened to the wind blowing in the chimney and saw that it had grown dark, the silhouettes of trees in the back garden mysterious against the dark blue, the waning moon reflected against the glass panes of a conservatory.

'Well, it'll be nice to be all in the same house again for a night, won't it? Victoria's at a friend's, she'll be back soon. I phoned up and told her you were here. She's dead excited!' said my mother, laughing her nervous laugh.

'I've hardly seen her for weeks. How's she doing at school?'

'Oh, fine. Yes, she's just been carrying on as usual. Her teachers are pleased with her. Your English teacher's been phoning to see how you're getting on. What's his name? Mr – '

'Thompson.'

'That's it! See, your memory's not that bad after all! The nurses said they thought you'd have forgotten a lot after what you've been through.'

'It's OK with some things I suppose . . .'

'Well, it'll all come back. Yep, you're on the recovery road now, kiddo,' she said, feigning an American accent and pouring tea with a steady trickle into a blue and white china teacup, sighing as though she had attained it by intravenous means, poured in the milk and added a sweetener, stirred and handed it to me.

After my tea, I was keen to continue my exploration. My mother told me dinner would be ready in an hour or so, and that I mustn't try to do too much. I opened the lounge door and stepped out into the hallway, then went up the stairs. Through the window, the trees of the coppice stood tall and skeletal, scraping the air as they swayed gently in the breeze. Walking around the staircase, I drifted automatically towards a dark corridor to the far end of the landing, bypassing three open doors to my right and a bathroom with a plush pink carpet as I turned left and down a short corridor, and turned the golden door handle at the end of it.

209

After I found the light switch, the room lit up and it was as though I had entered a dream. The cream walls, pastel green curtains and carpet, the red, green and blue tartan quilt across the bed, the large wooden bookcase filling the wall to my right, the ENGLAND poster hanging on the wall ... Everything seemed to be lurching toward me and sucking me in, suffocatingly intense. The walls spun, and I sat heavily on the floor and tried to understand what was happening.

Presently the dizziness subsided and I could walk with greater certainty. I tried to work out what this all meant. The bed was neatly made and the posters on the walls represented cricket and rugby, my two favourite sports. Had someone collected objects together and placed them here for me to enjoy? Had my vision of Westmoreland finally reaped its rewards?

I looked at a framed school photograph, 'Yarm School 1991' in gold lettering beneath it. To the top left I could see my younger self. I concluded that perhaps I must have gone backwards in time to 1991 as I remembered the photograph had been taken recently. But as I looked in the mirror above a pale-green sink close to the door, the face looking back at me was much older and less cheerful.

The books on the shelf included familiar titles. There were many children's books, from the likes of Arthur Ransome, Roald Dahl, Enid Blyton. Books on astronomy, ornithology and wildlife, science and history ... Many Penguin 60s, amongst them a book of seven short stories by James Herriot, which I felt sure I had sent to Susan Lefting. Many books of poetry, volumes of Coleridge and Wordsworth, Shakespeare texts .... And beneath all of these, in the bottom layer of the bookcase, I found school exercise books and files. I pulled one out, marked SCIENCE in the top left corner in red felt tip capitals. In the right corner, in scruffy fountain pen ink, read: 'James Fountain: 1B'. It was a shock to see my name written by my own hand. And as I raked through the dusty books and read over my old classroom notes I was waking slowly from a dream, regaining fragments of memory. With a little effort I could vividly recall writing each page of notes, copying things from teachers' blackboards, struggling to get it all down fast enough. Being told off for talking and having to stand outside on a freezing winter's day.

I delved further and further back. I found a poem called 'Autumn' I had written at West Park Primary on leaf-shaped paper and mounted on brown and yellow card, dated 'October 1987'. Another one was there too, written a year later, 'Magic Apple', which I remembered had won a prize in a creative writing competition three years afterwards at Yarm. I remembered my mother sitting over dinner persuading me to enter it, against my loud protestations. I found logbooks I had kept on solitary birdwatching expeditions between six and eight years of age, some from when I had briefly rekindled an interest in ornithology at the age of ten; notes on astronomy from a school television programme.

I looked through photo albums, and amongst them found shots of my eighth birthday held at Park Place restaurant in Stockton and was reminded of how I'd blown it with a girl that day and how it had been so important to me at the time that I had lain awake all night regretting how I had frozen up, and how she'd barely spoken to me after. The pangs of guilt jabbing at my insides confirmed for me that this had happened. This was my room, this was my stuff, and these were my memories, slowly coming back.

Suddenly, I heard my mother call me from the end of the corridor, and then enter the room. She looked at the piles of exercise books and files scattered across the floor. She spoke to me as if I were a spoilt child playing with toys that had previously been cast aside. But I knew she was just trying to be supportive. I was beginning to understand what a tough thing it was for her, for me to have been away from home all this time.

211

'Oh, you're having a little look at all your old schoolbooks! Is it helping to jog your memory?'

'Yes. I remember now ...'

'Can you remember the last night you spent in here? The room was a tip, so I've tidied it all up for you. There were books everywhere, pieces of paper you'd scribbled on ...'

'I thought all that stuff happened at Hartlepool General?'

'No, it started here, then carried on and on. But I think we've turned the corner now. Everything'll be back to normal soon, you'll see. Anyway, your dinner's ready, so if you'd like to come down, I'll put it on the table.'

As I'd thought, the kitchen was the room with the Formica tops. My memory seemed to have sharpened somewhat, and the white wallpaper with varicoloured floral designs upon it, and the hexagonal wooden table at which I sat seemed familiar and comforting. The fire was on, and the atmosphere was cosy and rich with the smell of Sunday roast, whilst the windows were tipped with a layer of frost around their edges, like something out of a Dickens novel.

We all tucked in, and my sister was telling me about an argument she'd been having with kids at school.

'I keep telling them you got spiked with LSD, you didn't take it yourself. They're such bitches!'

'Victoria! Watch that language!' exclaimed my father, shocked as ever that any of us could possibly venture to swear.

'Well, they are, I've never liked those girls. Of course my friends are more sensible, but Debby Pridham of all people!'

'Ah, well. I don't care really,' I said. 'I mean, I do, but worrying about them's not going to get me home is it? When I'm in hospital reading my get well cards the people who wrote them seem so far away. They wouldn't understand what I've been through, even though they think they do.'

Silence fell suddenly amongst us, and I realised I'd killed the conversation. It was my great weakness: I always spoke my mind. I knew that I spoke for all of us, but it was as though I had uttered something that previewed the struggle ahead. But at the same time, I knew that this little speech acknowledged and heralded my resolve to accept people's concern for my well being, but to reject the ideas of those who lived in perpetual ignorance. How many people did we know who had openly admitted that they had spent time in a psychiatric ward, for whatever reason? Not many.

'Food's good, isn't it, James? I think I've cooked it just right again!' my mother laughed, breaking the deadlock.

'Ah, yes, it's nice to be home,' I said, imitating the voice of a tired old traveller.

As I lay in bed that night with the lights out, I listened to the sound of wind in the tall trees across the road, and wondered what the future might bring. Whether it would be possible to slot back into the world like a piece of God's great jigsaw, back into my school society, uniform-clad like the others, shining as brightly as the five hundred or so other bulbs connected in series, ready to take on the voltage of work. I gazed into the darkness and wondered if my light had been dimmed by recent events. And then I realised that I would never let this happen, that I'd absorbed plenty of knocks before, and like Mohammed Ali in the *Rumble in the Jungle*, I would take these blows to the head, and when I got my chance, come off the ropes, and knock my opponent out.

20

In the morning I awoke and went down for breakfast, having slept soundly through the night. The sun was out and the daffodils vivid against the tall conifers at the far end of the garden as I looked out at them from the kitchen table. Blue tits came to eat nuts from the feeders, fighting amongst themselves, and male blackbirds hopped around their respective territories, cocking their heads to the ground as they listened for worms. A robin arrived on the bird table and nervously prodded the breadcrumbs on offer, taking a piece then flying away to eat it elsewhere. A collared dove perched on the edge of the stone water bowl, arching back its proud grey head to savour the cool water.

Slowly the mist of sleep cleared to leave fragments of dreams, mostly composed of an elaborate network of faltering early childhood and revelations of the future. I tried to explain them to my mother while she cooked me a bacon sandwich.

'There was a moment where I was sleepwalking, everyone was asleep, and I was creeping out of the front door and getting into a car and driving away, and then suddenly I was much older and driving the same car and remembering the same dream ...'

'How strange,' she remarked.

'And in another dream, I was afraid of someone who had broken into the house with a shotgun and I was opening the window and jumping out of it, sprouting white wings in mid-air, turning into a dove and flying away.'

'There's a lot about flight in these dreams, like you want to escape something.'

'Yes, I think so. Like I'm trying to escape from myself.'

'Well, I suppose that's understandable. But it'll pass. You

feel alright, don't you?'

'Yeah, of course.'

After I had eaten a bacon sandwich and drunk a cup of tea, I showered, got dressed and packed up the few things I had brought with me. On the journey back to the hospital my mother gave me advice about being sensible and doing whatever the doctor and nurses said, that I should take my time and that I was not going to get better overnight. I said I would try my best to do all she had suggested, whilst admitting it was going to be hard being 'normal' again.

Charlotte was waiting beside the lift when I returned.

'Hiya, James! How did it go?'

'Oh, he was fine. You were a little bit confused at first, though, weren't you?' asked my mother.

'Well! 'E's bound to be, after all. But apart from that he was fine?'

'Oh yes, no problems.'

I felt invisible. They were talking about me as though I was no longer there, so I drifted back to my room with my rucksack and flung it on the bed. I sat in the armchair and switched on the TV. The lunchtime edition of *Neighbours* was just beginning, with its ludicrously camp soundtrack. I sank into the mundane world of soap opera Oz and tried to imagine being back in a similar world containing all the various delights of school, birthdays, and relationships that are great for a few weeks then mysteriously disintegrate. Instead I wanted Dr Norton and the nurses to give me back that world they'd taken from me, with all its blank despair and rollercoaster rides. I wanted the challenge back, like a drug addict thinking himself into a relapse. I wanted my madness back.

Later that afternoon, Lizzie came into the room and informed me that my friend Ben Tillett would be coming to see me in the evening.

'Your mum told me you've had an up and down friendship

over the years, so I'll not let 'im stay too long in case he upsets you, OK?' I couldn't believe what I was hearing.

'No, it's not OK! He's my friend and he can stay as long as he bloody wants!'

'Don't use that tone of voice with me, young man! I'm just tryin' to do my job, and your mother thinks that it'd be best if Ben didn't stay too long.'

'Great. You do your job then. And don't bring me any more pills just 'cos I'm sick of everyone ordering me around. They're making me so tired I can barely move.'

'James, we're just tryin' to help ye, that's all.'

'Well don't. And don't try and help my friends either. They're as normal as I want them to be.'

'What does that mean, James?'

'Oh, just go away. I'm sick of having to explain everything.'

Lizzie stood glaring at me for a moment, then turned to walk out, and for a moment I saw her head morph into a terrifying, bestial, wolfish form, with angry red eyes and threatening fangs. As she turned round momentarily in the doorway the beast's head transformed magically into her own. I was delighted. It seemed that everything was not going to be quite so normal after all.

Ben Tillett arrived shortly after I had eaten dinner. His dull, pompous parents told him they would be back in three quarters of an hour, eyed my thin frame with circumspection, then got back into the lift as though there was something fatally contagious floating about the ward, or a vile smell.

Ben was dressed in a white, V-necked shirt and jet-black jeans, tall and slightly overweight as usual, which had always come in handy whenever he had felt like smashing against my bony body during rugby practice. But today his sky-blue eyes were genial and mild, his countenance genuine and apologetic. As we walked up to the lounge after I had made us some tea, his remarkably thin lips delivered tales of school, of schoolboy humiliation, of practical jokes and his adventures with drugs and drink, all of which seemed far away and mundane.

'I mean, Stan an' me, we've being tryin' LSD now an' then for ages, man, and we've 'ad nothin' 'appen to us like what's 'appened to you. People would pay good money to be trippin' their bollocks off all the time like you are!'

'Oh, it's not all fun ... but yeah, I see what you're getting at. Some of it's been pretty amazing ... But I don't know if it would suit everybody.'

'Yeah, but that's the great thing about it though, isn't it? I mean all that stuff, all hallucinogens. It depends on your mood when you take them, your personality ...' Suddenly I shuffled forward in my seat and lowered my voice.

'Do you know who did this to me?'

'No, man. Some names came up at one time but I reckon it's all bullshit. No one at our school would do anythin' like that. No one would waste good drugs.'

'You're sure? I think you might be wrong there.'

'Well, ye never know I suppose ... an' you were never that popular were ye really?' Unlike him, I thought. 'But I didn't go to the ball, so I can't comment. I saw nowt. The police came round interviewin' people, everyone who went the night it 'appened. Apparently, one or two of the Teesside High girls saw someone puttin' drugs in your drink, but they won't tell anyone but the police who it was they saw.'

I looked him carefully in the eye. I did not suspect Ben. I had known him since he was four, and though he'd gotten all competitive since he began at Yarm School, and was harsh at times in his attitude towards me, our friendship had picked up over the past year or so. Anyway, I knew who it was. And I knew why those Teesside High girls were not overly keen to reveal any names.

'Let's play table tennis,' I suggested, as a sudden silence had fallen, mostly because I had drifted into troubled introspection.

Ben wanted to play a game rather than rallies, and as time

wore on his competitiveness grew, so that memories of past arguments seeped like poison into my mind. As I hit a return past him, his next serve belted past me, and it was as though he had forgotten where I was, and begun to think that I was there to be beaten. His blue eyes burned with determination, he pulled his T-shirt from his jeans to give him greater freedom of movement, and I decided to let him win. No game with Ben was ever just a game.

By the time Ben's parents returned, preferring to shout his name from the lift area rather than venture into the ward, I was glad to let him go. I shook his hand and thanked him for coming, but was shaking somewhat, bitterly disappointed that, even now, we could not quite manage to make our way back to the friendship we once had.

'Thanks for the card, too.'

'Oh, no worries, man. Take care o' yeself, and hopefully we'll see ye back at school soon!'

'You never know.'

'See ye.'

I stood watching him walk down the corridor to his parents, who were waving at me in the distance as if I were a leper. I had been cast off from society to drift in years of solitude, with only occasional visits from friends whom I thought I once knew, but could no longer be sure. I spiralled down into a high-backed chair, and felt wave after wave of disappointment moving towards me, curled up, and let the tears come.

Sheila was just finishing her shift, but she must have heard the sobs. Through the hot smudges of darkness and light I felt her hands taking mine away from my face, her voice soothing and dreamlike through the flashes of conversation that swirled like a merry-go-round through my mind: cinematic remakes of arguments with friends and girlfriends, Rachel's rejection of me, missed opportunities, lost love. There was no way out of the labyrinth. Never again would I be free like Ben, I could see it now. Every thought that entered seemed to compound this certainty, and drew me further down a slowly winding coil of despair.

'It's alright,' Sheila said, gently rocking me in her arms.

In this protective embrace, my eyes gradually cleared, though a dark uncertainty remained. Suddenly breaking free, I wandered absentmindedly down the corridor, the dusky doorways like trees lining a never-ending pathway to my room. Switching on the light, the objects about my room seemed to weigh me down, as though myriad emotions had metamorphosed into lifeless forms. These included Susan's letter, lying on the table, tempting me to read her kind, sincere words that held little promise of returning anything other than mere friendship. The spectre of her saddened, tear-drenched face drifted out from the lift and hung in the space above her assured handwriting. The cards that covered the wall echoed a widespread, yet distant concern, like the faces of a supporting crowd that knew nothing of the sport they were watching.

So I began to take them down. Each card I removed was one less pair of eyes to follow me about the room, one less layer of expectancy. I paused briefly to look at a section I had devoted to anonymous well-wishers, a nameless streak of humanity that somehow felt they could help. But at that moment they seemed nothing more than intruders, their innocent-looking notes reminding me of my entrapment and their freedom.

As I scratched the final pieces of Blu Tac from the wall, the pressure eased. I stacked up the cards and put them in the cupboard beside my bed. I heard breathing behind me and turned around in a sudden panic that perhaps I had done something wrong.

'Eh, what've ye done with all yer cards, James?' asked Peter, dressed in a dark-blue shirt and pale-blue tie, standing in the doorway with his tall, powerful frame, peering at the wall.

'I've taken them down. I had to do it, I was tired of them all watching me.'

'Watching ye? How can cards *watch* ye? They're just things!'

'Look, I'm not going to argue. But it's true. People expect too much of me, when they don't realise that people are keeping me here. I'll spend the rest of my life in here, and they won't understand why. And they don't know what it's like!'

'Look, son, calm down. You'll get better, don't worry. Ye've gotta try to relax, stop movin' about all the time, ye know?'

'Let me get past then. I'm going to watch some TV. If I'm allowed, that is.'

'Eh, stop this, of course you're allowed. Just don't walk so quickly everywhere, that's all.'

As if to prove a point, I sat up until 4.00 a.m. watching TV, barely moving a muscle throughout. After two or three extra tablets and two sleeping tablets, Anna and Peter finally insisted that I go to bed, and I complied with their wishes.

But it was still dark when I woke, and I knew I had failed to sleep a sufficient amount to keep everyone happy with my progress. I had slipped up somewhere.

When Dr Norton entered the room I was still in my dressing gown, polishing the lenses of my glasses with one of the sleeves, thinking the smudginess of my sight had been caused by unclean lenses. But, replacing them once more on my nose, I realised my sight was blurred from exhaustion. Perched on the armchair, I could only guess what Dr Norton would make of it all.

'Well, James, how are you? Oh, you've taken all the cards off your wall. Why's that?'

'Well ... I just ... I don't know, I just didn't want them looking at me all the time and making me feel guilty.'

'Guilty?'

'Yes. I just wanted to get better on my own. They made me feel guilty for not getting better quickly enough. Made me feel like a nutter.'

'Let's get this straight. Today's the sixth of March. You've been a patient here for twenty days, almost three weeks. Before that you were at St Luke's for nine days, and before

220

that Hartlepool General for three or four days. I'm not pretending this has been easy for you. But your time spent straightening these problems out now will hold you in good stead for the rest of your life. Now that you're a bit better, we can maybe talk about this illness that you have in more depth ...' The words came slowly but decisively toward me through the sedated haze like ships navigating their way through a fog.

'Right. And – what is the – illness?' I asked, tentatively.

'You have hypomania, a hybrid form of manic depression, which was probably sparked off by the LSD in your drink, though this cannot be proven due to the strange disappearance of the blood sample. A urine sample indicated the presence of an unknown substance, though this would not stand up in court, as it is only ninety nine per cent proof. But leaving that incident aside, you have a mood affective disorder, which often affects those of creative, expansive minds. And so writers, artists, playwrights and so on, often get this illness, along with successful businessmen. Many of my patients have done very well for themselves, and others – they create jobs and generate cash flow within the community. You have a powerful imagi- nation, which, as we have discussed before, has at times sparked hallucinogenic episodes, both auditory – where you can hear things that aren't there – and visual. You have increased energy, which explains all the nights of lost sleep and your previous lack of concentration. But I would say that all of this has improved, wouldn't you?'

'I suppose ... Though I don't think I'm quite there yet.' Honesty was the best policy, however much it hurt.

'No, but not far off. I think we can have you home for a couple of nights again next week, and we'll take it from there. Your mother said you were fine when you went home last time. Would you agree?'

'Yes, apart from the fact I'd forgotten what the house looked like, and my room and all my things.'

221

'Well, that can happen. But the memory's sorting itself out now?'

'Yes, I think so, bit by bit.'

'Good. Well, just remember to tell your friends you had a touch of the Virginia Woolf when you eventually see them at school. She had the same illness as you have – except in her day there wasn't a cure, poor woman. Right, see you tomorrow!' And then he slapped me on the knee, said something about me needing to eat a bit more, and went off into the corridor.

The next day, Julian Welsh came to visit. I was delighted to see him, though a strange, light-headed mood had come over me shortly before his arrival. We sat over a cup of tea, and Julian initially talked of the ski trip I had missed and all the course work he had been doing for his GCSEs, that he had no idea how I would be able to catch up. His father sat over his shoulder, rustling a broadsheet, fresh from work in a smart, pinstriped suit, thin and fit in appearance, though slightly haggard in the face with thin, wispy grey hair that was oddly out of sync with the rest of him.

Suddenly I found myself launching into a retelling of all the wonders I had discovered. I took Julian on a guided tour of the ward. As I explained to him, we were in actual fact aboard a ship, and I was to be trained as its navigator. To my left I pointed out the small toilet whose door swung both ways – far from conventional, and evidently part of the ship's safety system, to protect the user of the toilet if there should be a flood, for example. Walking back up to the lounge, I took Julian over to the rear window and pointed out the red lights which transmitted the ship's security communications and guarded against intruders, or flash and draw attention if a raid took place.

'I – don't think so James ...' Julian began.

'Ah, but look!' I said excitedly, hell-bent on persuading my friend of my brilliant discovery, which I realised was concealed from those lacking the creative imagination to see it.

I showed him the quiet room with the cupboard of painting equipment, and pointed out an elaborate crystal vase, which I assured him was worth thousands of pounds, and was mine to keep once I had resided on-board for a year and gained the qualification of ship's navigator. Julian looked at me in disbelief, and I saw he was beyond convincing. But I was in no mood to be deterred from my course of thinking, and I let him add himself to the growing crowd of disbelievers. When finally he left with his father, it felt as though I had put something away in that cupboard beside my bed along with those well-wishing cards that was more significant than I had first imagined. I had put away other people's images of me, and begun to concentrate on who I really was.

Six days later, Dr Norton deemed I was well enough to go home for two nights, and so that morning, 12 March, I was once more phoning home and announcing triumphantly that I had won the chance to return home for a second spell. To this point I could see the need to employ tactics, to police any stray thoughts and conversation that might betray underlying weaknesses. I could tell my sanity was hanging by a thin, fraying thread, and at times I had to dismiss thoughts that I was God's special agent, as a professional footballer must resist the urge to retaliate when bombarded by vicious insult from an opponent or supporter in the crowd.

But I was homeward-bound, and this time the car journey seemed more familiar than the last, though memories were still in the process of repair, like a cathedral whose roof has been shelled. As my mother's little white Peugeot buzzed along, I settled contentedly into the seat, my mother giving words of encouragement, certain now that the big day of my release was near.

We headed into Hartlepool past the colourful pre-war town houses of Grange Road, and the ugly red seventies-style council buildings, the contrastingly beautiful Grand Hotel, then turned through the network of traffic-lights on to Church Street. My mother explained she had booked a hairdressing appointment for me, and as I ran my fingers through strands that went down to my shoulders, I realised she had been right to do so.

Sitting in the comfortable, black leather hairdresser's chair, the modern salon humming with conversation, customers and hairdressers talking about families and the weather, I fell asleep, lulled by the hypnotic movement of the scissors' blades. When he'd finished cutting my hair I thanked the hairdresser, and my mother paid him at the counter.

'Ah, that's better isn't it, James?' said my mother, examining my newly trimmed locks. I nodded.

'I hope everything'll go well for you all from now on,' said the hairdresser. 'I know it's been a tough old time for you all, but it'll come good, you'll see.'

'Oh, thanks a lot, Dave. Yeah, we could do with a bit o' luck. Poor James has been through hell the last few weeks, and we have too.'

'I know, I feel sorry for you, I know a lot of people do. Well, best of luck,' Dave said.

'Thanks, Dave. See ya!' said my mother, quickly ushering me out the door and into the car. 'Dave cuts your father's hair, and he used to cut yours. You can't remember, can you?' she asked. I nodded, still too tired to talk. 'We don't want to attract too much attention. The police and the press still want to see you, and we don't want them to. You're not well enough.'

Back home, my mother and I whiled away the afternoon in the lounge with the fire on, the wind howling against the windows as we watched Hitchcock's version of *The Thirty-Nine Steps* on BBC2. By the end I was making connections between the film and my own life, and saw interesting parallels between Buchan's portrayal of espionage between the wars and my own secret existence relaying communications from God. I allowed the levels of policing to be lowered, and found myself believing with renewed conviction in all the things I had striven to extinguish from my mind. I decided that, like spies, some things had to be believed in, even if you could not see them.

21

My mother had hired *A River Runs Through It* for us to watch as a family, and when my sister came back from school we all had dinner then moved into the study. I watched the images of two brothers growing up in the rolling Montana landscape and the Big Black Foot River and could see a resemblance between the aspirations of the narrator Norman Maclean and my own, as he went on to do an English Literature degree and then to teach at the University of Chicago. I had forgotten my true purpose, and here it was, indicated to me again. The excesses of his brother Paul counterbalanced his elder brother's seriousness, which I supposed inspired Robert Redford to make the film, though I felt that I would be more likely to become a combination of the two, just serious enough to get by and succeed.

I took the ideas on board, and as I went up to bed that night, wishing my mother, father, and sister goodnight, my mind fizzed with possibility. I was 16 years old, with everything to look forward to, and everything to do. So much time had been wasted. I sat on the edge of my bed and counted up the days I had been away from school. February 2 seemed so long ago that I concluded it must have been a year and 40 days ago. This made sense. And that would mean my first A level year was well over half way through, and I had not even begun my studies. I saw my school files lying in the bookcase and realised I had wasted too much time already.

I moved over to the walk-in wardrobe and opened the white door. Raking through the clothes, I picked out the jacket my mother had purchased for the purpose of sixth form, a white shirt, my school tie, a pair of grey school trousers, grey socks and shining black shoes, and proceeded to get dressed. I found the Caterpillar record bag and filled it with whatever files on the bookcase I thought might be of use. English, History and German – they were the subjects I would study. Then I sat on the bed and waited for morning.

Seconds later, my mother entered the room in her dressing gown. She had evidently been asleep, and looked aghast.

'James! What are you doing? It's one o'clock in the morning!'

'I've decided to go back to school,' I said.

'Oh, no you're not. You'll take off those clothes and go back to bed. And anyway it would be too early, wouldn't it? School starts at nine. And you've got the wrong uniform on! Now go back to bed!' She watched me begin to undress, then left the room.

I considered. Perhaps it was just my imagination. Perhaps she was right, a year had not passed after all, it just seemed that way. So on returning to the wardrobe I took out my blue, police-style navy woollen jumper with velcro epaulettes on either shoulder, which was part of the school uniform, and one of the light-blue school shirts, which also had epaulettes. I attached a light-blue and navy chequered house flash to the right shoulder epaulette of the jumper and shirt, then put them on with the tie and grey trousers and shoes. I looked in the mirror. Now I was ready.

Again my mother burst into the room, this time more urgent and irritated in her speech.

'Right, James, what are you doing now? You can't go back to school tomorrow, I won't allow it until you're properly better. You understand?'

'No! I'm fine. There's nothing wrong with me.'

My mother held her head in her hands, as though it were becoming heavy.

'OK ... tablets. I think you need another tablet to make you sleep. Just a second.'

She disappeared and I reached into the wardrobe to find

another costume. I quickly pulled on the evening suit I'd worn at a ball before Christmas, hoping this would be sufficient to lull my mother out of giving me more tablets. She liked to see me in my evening suit. Through a dreamlike state of consciousness, I undressed and began to dress again, and it seemed like hard work. I was just buttoning up the white shirt as my mother came back.

'Oh, take that off! Look, your father's trying to sleep next door, he's got work in the morning. Now take this tablet.'

'No, I – '

'Go on!'

At her insistence, I took the glass of orange juice offered and reluctantly drank down the tablet with its chalky aftertaste.

'Right – take those clothes off and get into bed, and go – to – sleep. OK? Night, darling.'

She kissed me on the head, and as she left the room I began to do as she said. Turning off the light, I got under the quilt and lay there wondering what I had been doing. I was finally becoming conscious of a lack of control, a momentary merging of time and place. It seemed clear there was a straight choice between semi-consciousness and consciousness, between the surreal and reality.

When I found I couldn't sleep I was filled with panic. I thought of what chaos the morning might bring if I failed to sleep. In the darkness I crept toward the window and pulled back the curtain to reveal pale streetlights, orange ones lighting the road to Elwick visible through the black outlines of coppice trees swaying to and fro. I gazed at a pool of rainwater by the road reflecting the white light like a ghost. A white polythene bag floated past in the strong wind, which whirred in the panes of glass as if the plastic and the liquid ghosts were enjoying a secret conversation.

It did not seem long before the sky grew lighter, and the birds proclaimed the beginning of another day. I knew there and then, as the sun was rising in the east to the right of the coppice, that I would go back to the hospital a day early, and that I may never come home again.

I sat down to breakfast, numb with tiredness and the desolation of the recent past.

'I'll go back today then,' I said to my mother as she placed down my cooked breakfast, still in her white dressing gown as I'd seen her hours earlier, 'I think it's best.'

'Oh, are you sure? I was looking forward to having you home a couple of days. You seem OK now.'

'I don't know. I think I should go back.'

She sat down and faced her boiled egg as though she were staring someone down. Then she picked up her spoon and tapped the top with it, the tip of the spoon shaking from the vibrations of her hand.

'Right. After breakfast I'll take you along.'

'OK.'

'I'm sorry you're not well. I just want everything to be back to normal.' As she spoke her face gradually creased up, and she cried long and loudly into her hands. And I did nothing, just sat and watched the episode as if she were a soap star on TV, except it hurt. It hurt that I was hurting people, it hurt that I could do nothing to relieve their suffering. It hurt that I knew what was wrong and could do nothing about it.

Depression descended like a blanket over us, but was punctuated by the sudden entrance of my Aunty Beryl. I had not heard the front door closing, and she came happily in through the kitchen door, wrapped up warm in a pink scarf and navy blue jacket with a green collar.

'Oh, hello! I knew you were home, so I thought I'd pop round. How are you, then? Barbara, what's wrong?'

'He's going back to the hospital, Beryl. He doesn't feel very well,' said my mother, wiping the tears from her face.

'Oh, come here,' my aunty hugged me briefly, 'you'll be alright. Just give it time.'

'I suppose ... hey, are you pregnant?'

229

Shock waves seemed to flow in the glances between the two sisters.

'Beryl? You never told me!' said my mother.

'How did you know that, James?' she asked me. 'I am, but I've only been for a couple of weeks.'

'Ah,' I said. 'I don't know.'

My mother hugged my aunty, as did I, a strange and special moment.

The journey back was as devoid of joy as a car journey could be. My mother was crying all the way and I held my head in shame, as if I had admitted to a great crime and was being driven direct to prison to prevent an unnecessary hearing. But I knew I was not well, and there was nothing more to say.

Back at the hospital, Dr Norton was waiting, and took me and my mother down to the office. As I sat in one of the two chairs, nervously eyeing the typewriter and remembering what it once meant, the doctor unveiled a new plan.

'I think we'll try him on lithium. From what you've told me over the phone, it's obvious that the present medication's not working.' My mother nodded slowly, her face grey and lined as if she had missed many nights of sleep. 'And the second thing I suggest we do is have James isolated for a week. That means no visits from anyone, family, friends or anyone else, for seven days.'

'Oh, are you sure that's necessary?' my mother asked, a little surprised.

'Absolutely. I'm afraid it's absolutely necessary. These are the last two things we can try. Or your son may never get better. I'm sorry.'

'OK then, let's do it. Chris and I are completely behind you.' I could tell she was trying to be brave and keep composed in front of the doctor, who commanded respect in his obvious dedication to the cause. But I felt strangely detached from the scene, as though I were a ghost observing my mother arranging my funeral proceedings with an undertaker.

After this interview, my mother made a tearful departure, hugging me tightly, sobbing that she could feel all of the ribs in my back and making me promise that I would eat more.

Back in my room, the silence built up, brick by brick. I could stand no music, nothing whatever that reminded me of the outside world I had once felt part of. It had rejected me. From the window I looked upon the high deciduous oaks and beeches with disgust, imagining the younger self that with half an opportunity would have climbed up their branches, agile and free, with no fear of falling.

But now I had fallen.

I sat for two or three hours gazing unblinkingly at the TV screen, which was humming slightly on mute. I watched newsreaders on Sky News reading out the same stories over and over again, then the staff rotated and the new ones read the same stories again. And through the dullness came my master plan, and as it formed, my spirits brightened. All was not lost.

I leapt up and ran into the corridor and smashed the red and black glass box. The fire alarm screeched out in ear-blasting waves of sound. Panic followed as I stood and watched the nurses flying down the corridor to get the two or three old patients up and out of their rooms. I hurried to take my chance, trying in vain to squeeze open the elevator doors with a waning strength, as there was no key with which to open them. I would have to make a copy.

But then I felt arms closing around me pulling me away, and then the alarm was switched off and Lizzie was shouting, 'Don't do that again!', and I was back in my room.

Over the next few days, the fog of depression steadily cleared. There were walks to Jesmond Dene, and one afternoon Charlotte allowed me to have a look in some of the little shops at the approach to the dene. I knew Mother's Day was approaching, so I went into a shop in which I had noticed a beautiful silver brooch I knew my mother would appreciate, and bought it. The wonderfully mystic shop owner, who constantly burned incense behind her counter, kindly wrapped the brooch in elaborate paper for me, gold teeth gleaming between pearly-whites as she smiled.

'I love your shop,' I said, pausing to take in the marvellous and extensive array of exotic stationery and household items, all displayed upon rugs from the Far East, the walls purple and rouge.

'Ye, I've seen you in here a few times,' said the woman, her voice light and friendly, her dark eyes heavy and dreamy, 'you from round here?'

'Yes – for now. I'll come back again soon!'

'Oh, I hope so! Maybe find something nice for yourself next time,' she suggested.

'Thanks a lot,' said Charlotte as we walked out. This maddened me, her habit of apologising to all the shopkeepers, as if my brief presence within them had been some sort of burden. The madman poking around their wares looking at pretty little things.

But by now the lithium had taken effect, and with each passing day a new sense of harmony built up inside and around me. The psychological prison walls evaporated, and I found myself in genial conversation at every turn, greeting Lizzie cheerfully whenever she came with the next dose of tablets, and even reminding her when they were five or ten minutes overdue.

On Monday I visited a dermatologist on the second floor, a jovial, overweight man of around sixty with white hair, named Dr Smythe, at Dr Norton's recommendation. He prescribed medication that would clear up my acne within the next seven to ten days.

'– and then you'll have all the girls wanting to kiss you!' he joked, emitting warbling laughter which made it impossible not to join in.

Other checks were carried out – a brain scan, which tried my patience and lasted around half an hour, with all manner of tremendously loud hammering sounds coming at me from all angles. And at Lizzie's insistence I was weighed, and found I was just under 8 stone (50 kilos), and had lost 2 stone in weight. My legs were thin, devoid of muscle and ached constantly, and indeed my whole body ached. My thoughts were now sluggish and clouded, and each night I went to bed early to try to break free from the drowsy tiredness that I wore like an unremovable suit, and each day woke up feeling as though I had a blinding hangover.

And finally I accepted it – the past, the present and all that was yet to come. I began to see the corner that had been turned, that everything had changed. Late Monday afternoon I sat staring at Rachel Lockwood's card in the fading light, and as the various pieces of the puzzle assembled themselves it became clear that my earlier suspicions were correct. Everything fit. And though the pain and anger had not yet quelled, I felt compelled to forgive and forget. We are all very young, after all, I thought. Through my silence they would learn my strength, that without saying a word I was the secret victor. I had beaten them, and was content to imagine that the boy in question could change his habits, or burn in hell. I no longer cared, either way. He knew who he was, and what he had done. Let it be.

22

By Thursday, Dr Norton was satisfied that I had recovered sufficiently to take a trip into Newcastle, as part of the 'process of reintegration'. The brain scan was normal, and the acne was receding with the help of the treatment Dr Smythe had prescribed. I telephoned my mother and she said it was all arranged, and that she and my Aunty Beryl would come and take me around the shopping centre and we could have some lunch.

They collected me around twelve o'clock, and I was delighted to see familial faces after eight days away from them. But by now it felt as though they were visiting my home. My room had become a flat rather than a cell, and as such I felt no desperate desire to be 'reintegrated'. But I knew it must be done.

Before we left, I gave my mother her parcel.

'It's for Mother's Day, last Sunday,' I explained. Suddenly her face brightened tenfold, and her eyes resembled a happy child's.

'Oh, you remembered! Thanks very much!' She carefully unwrapped the paper, and tears came instantly to her eyes when she saw the brooch. 'Oh, thank you. Come here!' But as she hugged me, I realised nothing could truly repay the gratitude I felt. If I had a mother of lesser patience and character I may have been cast out, and never recovered. Now, as I stood on the brink, I remembered stories I had read of people who had been ostracized from their families due to the perceived embarrassment or taboo of psychiatric illness, and subsequently been sent on a downward spiral of despair, never to return. I thanked my stars this had not happened to me.

Outside, a light drizzle hung in the air like confetti. As my mother drove us out of Jesmond and into Newcastle city centre, people seemed to be standing at traffic-lights waiting to receive the prodigal son, the survivor. The emotion that swelled inside me was immense, the hum of the city like a vast engine with all the cogs and wheels of humanity driving it on, a world I was about to re-enter after a long period of absence. It seemed odd to think that this momentous occasion was taking place, and yet no one looking through the car windows even knew who I was. The world of Newcastle had moved on, a pub had changed its name, a café was now boarded up, and the road bore new markings, which confused my mother. And through my sixteen-year-old mind flashed the haunting realisation that when someone was removed from the world, life rolled inexorably on, and a person could become forgotten.

My mother parked the car on the roof of a multi-storey car-park, and together with my Aunty Beryl and my little cousin Richard we got into an elevator. As we descended, I felt the noise of the shopping centre coming towards me, and felt ready to pass out as the noise swirled about me. But seconds later I was more secure, and as we stepped into the bright complex and busy pre-Easter crowd I felt bewildered but unpanicked. My mother noticed my anxiety and put her hand in mine.

'Disney Store!' shrieked Richard excitedly, jumping half his height into the air, his features awash with joy. My Aunty Beryl looked at my mother and by some telepathic fraternal communication we crossed Eldon Square from the lift and entered the shop.

Once inside the enormous shop, Richard ran quickly down the central aisle, pointing at something he had always wanted, his birthday not far off. I had never been in a Disney Store, and I found myself walking very slowly, mesmerised by the sight of row upon row of the same brightly coloured product, thousands of Mickey Mouse soft toys filling a long row, followed by a row of Minnie Mouse soft toys, followed by a row of Donald Ducks ... And as I looked down the immaculately laid out shelves with mirrors at the end of them, it appeared I had entered a hall of mirrors. My head spun, the dizziness I'd previously experienced tripled, and I fell to the floor.

After ten minutes, the glass of water the shop assistant offered revived me, and we were back on our way. My mother conceded it was perhaps too much, that even for her the shop was quite intense, with its loud music and never-ending rows of toys.

I took a look at a couple of CD shops I remembered while my mother and Aunty Beryl hovered in the doorway, and then they took a look in Marks & Spencer. After this Richard was complaining he wanted some pizza, so we found a Pizza Hut. My early dizziness had not returned, and all was well. The restaurant hummed with activity, customers leaving and new ones rolling in continuously. I caught Richard eyeing the balloon-strings held by small children like himself running hither and thither along the aisles, and demanded one of his own from his mother. A pair of businessmen by the ceiling to floor window looked out at the passing traffic trying to seem oblivious to the noise of children passing by them, pretty waitresses trying their best to dodge past with trays of pizzas and drinks.

Through the window I could see a beggar feeding tiny pieces of pizza crust to a group of grateful pigeons, the dirty skin around his eyes wrinkling as he smiled and squatted down to watch them gather round the crumbs.

Soon we were back at the car, and as I sat through the return journey, I felt utterly exhausted. On reaching the ward, I let my mother answer Lizzie's questions of concern, and lay my stiff body on the bed.

'Well! That wasn't too bad, was it?' asked my mother as she walked in a few minutes later.

'No, I enjoyed it. It was just a bit much that's all, I feel absolutely knackered.'

'I know. It's like that when you've been away from busy places for a while. It was like that for me when I recovered from my crushed ankle. Lizzie tells me all the nurses are happy with you now, that you can come home tomorrow. Isn't that great?! You've done really well, James, we're all so proud of you! See you tomorrow then, and thanks for my brooch, that was a nice thought.'

'Thanks for a lovely day.'

'And hopefully you've got many more to come. See you tomorrow, darling.'

And then she was gone, and I fell asleep.

After an early evening chat with Peter and Anna, who had become good friends, I drifted back to my room and slept as soundly as I had done the previous few nights, thoughts no longer crowding my mind, simply a feeling of gratitude and mental exhaustion.

Shortly after breakfast, and pleasant words with Laura, Pat and Betsy over a cigarette, who told me they were delighted I had recovered so quickly, my mother arrived to take me home.

Grabbing my ready-packed rucksack, my mother talked briefly with the nurses before we got in the lift, and presently we were on our way home.

'Your Aunty Jane's come all the way up from Skipton to see you, James,' she said.

'Really?'

'Oh, yes, she said she wanted to come up now that you're so much better. She's brought some things for you to do.'

Aunty Jane was waiting by the front door as I walked in. She was unmarried and in her forties, tall and blue-eyed, wearing blue jeans and a navy blue jumper, her short brown hair shining and her healthy face lit with emotion.

'Hi, Aunty Jane!'

'Oh, James, how lovely to see you! And you look so well,' she said, hugging me gently as she always did.

'Thanks. It's nice to see you! But yes, I'm a lot better now.'

'Oh, you can see, can't you, Barbara? I'm so pleased.'

'Yes, it's been a very sudden turnaround, we're very lucky,' said my mother, taking off her coat. 'Come on, let's go through to the lounge and have a nice cup of tea.'

Rather than tea, my mother gave me a warm high-protein drink to help build up my wiry frame. As the fire crackled, I looked into Sheila Ball's powerfully desolate painting of Top Withens in Haworth and remembered running through similar countryside 20 miles away at my Grandma and Aunty Jane's house in Cross Hills. I'd always loved the bleakness of the Dales, their mysteriousness. I remembered looking at dark mansions through my grandmother's binoculars as an eight-year-old, and reading in the local paper that the owner of one of the mansions was unable to sell it as it was notoriously haunted. I would peer through the binoculars at night looking for supernatural presences, and would be sure that what I saw was not a reflection of light against the glass window pane, as my father would insist, but an evil spirit hovering menacingly above the mansion.

Nature held sway in the Dales, and it was the proud, muscular green landscape that lay through the panoramic windows at the rear of my grandmother's house that always gave me that feeling of minuteness, of insignificance in the grand scheme of things. It was like the endlessly intertwining branches of the many trees visible from the desk in my bedroom at home; life seemed infinitely complex. And it was on childhood visits to this simultaneously wonderful and grotesque landscape that I learnt about the true underlying depth of all existence, and that no one and nothing had or would ever reach an end to those depths.

As I remembered sledging in the snow with Victoria two or three years before, on the steep banks just beyond my grandmother's back garden, it was interesting to think that the freedom, which that day I had thought would last forever, had now come to an end. No longer would I trust everybody, or take anything for granted. Every breath of open air would be savoured with the remembrance that things might have been different had I not finally returned to earth. But though the painting made me consider the transient nature of things, my perceptions were not polluted so much that I felt imprisoned within. On the contrary, the artist's depiction of cloudless horizons spoke of endless possibility, infused with a sudden awareness that an innocence had been lost, and would never return.

'How's Grandma?' I asked Aunty Jane, realising I'd not seen her for a long time.

'Oh, she's fine, yes, you know, just doing the usual things, a bit of knitting, a bit of shopping.'

'Good.' Aunty Jane loved harmony. Like the rest of my father's side of the family, she never discussed anything that could be said to approach bad news. This way, life was a perpetual delight, with no dark corners and no menace. I could not recall any deep and meaningful conversations that my Grandmother or Aunty Jane had introduced. Taking part in a family conversation with them was like learning to ice skate: it was hard work, forced, and if at any point you should slip, there was no possibility that you would break through the surface. That side of the family were frozen up to such an extent that most felt emotion would never happen to reach the surface.

And so it was that my Aunty Jane listened considerately to my mother's description of my illness thus far, whilst never appearing to get emotionally involved. Lots of 'mms' and 'yeses', as well as the occasional 'I know'. But I have no doubt that she hardly understood my mother, and so I realised that certain aspects of my illness must be disguised, even from certain family members. It was not going to be an easy topic to discuss, even in the third person. It was clear my aunt did not want to hear the various ins and outs of manic depression; and for the first time I realised just how taboo the subject was.

'Well, he looks a lot better, now,' sighed my Aunty Jane,

looking across at me. I smiled back, 'and soon you'll all be together again.'

'Yes,' said my mother. 'We're very grateful to Dr Norton for getting him better so quickly. You didn't see him, Jane, but really he was very, very ill at one stage.'

Somewhat embarrassed, I concerned myself with the dogs. I encouraged Sooty to jump up, and he did so, stood on my thighs, then curled himself carefully into a little silver and black ball. His brother Sweep lay in front of the fire on his side, happily cooking himself.

'Yes, but I suppose you've got to put all of that behind you now, if you see what I mean. That way you can all get on with your lives.'

My mother looked at her and clasped her hands more tightly around her teacup, warming them. 'Well, we'll see. I suppose it's one step at a time with these things, isn't it?' said my mother, slowly.

After lunch, my aunt revealed some gifts she had bought me, a set of top-quality watercolour paints and a pad of thick, specialist watercolour paper, along with a couple of fine brushes. I was delighted and touched – my aunt was a very delicate artist and over the years had spent a lot of time with my sister and me, teaching us how to draw and paint. This was her way of helping.

And so, for the rest of the afternoon, my aunt and I sat at the dining-room table, painting. My aunt always concentrated on still life, and proceeded to paint a beautifully accurate miniature of a vase of flowers. My subject matter was quite different. From my imagination I painted a sprawling river, which flowed through the heart of the painting, with trees in the distance upon an uncertain horizon and pea-green river-banks. I worked hard on the shade of blue I would use for the river, settling upon a deep turquoise, with pale blue for the sky and a ray of sun shining through it.

But with the next picture I settled down to paint the first

hallucination I could remember. I wanted my aunt to understand. I painted dull buildings being replaced by trees and rolling countryside, the sky mixed and chaotic in a swirl of blues and blacks, oranges and yellows, the landscape of nature meeting a man-made metropolis in the centre of the page. Beneath this I scrawled the title 'East Meets West' and a large, sprawling signature. It was fun pretending to be an artist.

I explained to my aunt its significance, the vision that had inspired it, as though I were da Vinci or Van Gogh presenting his latest masterpiece.

'Ooh, it must have been awful for you, James,' she began, her voice laden with sympathy.

'Awful? It was great! Everything that I wanted to happen did, but only I could see it. I mean, I know now that this wasn't really happening, of course. But it seemed very real at the time – it was the most wonderful piece of drama I have ever seen. What I'm trying to say is, not all of this illness has been as bad or as frightening as you might think, that's all.'

'Well, I'm sure you're right ... It's a nice picture, anyway! Such pretty colours ...' she said, her voice tailing off.

The evening meal was cheerful and optimistic. Victoria revealed she had been receiving good grades at school, and my father's law deals had been successful as usual, one of the rare occasions on which I had ever heard him mention work. My Aunty Jane spoke of a welcome but growing work load as she had been recently appointed matron at Airedale Hospital, with all its extra responsibilities.

And when Dr Norton rang later that night to suggest I stay on at home for the remainder of the weekend, the optimism generated was undiluted. I went to bed that night content that the storm had finally calmed, and the next day delved back into my childhood, painting pictures of a robin and a swallow with the aid of one of my old illustrated books on ornithology. Allowing these creative impulses to take flight was proving effective therapy, however imperfect their outcome.

23

On Monday I returned to the hospital, taking with me some of my GCSE files and exercise books at Dr Norton's suggestion. It was time to begin the process of relearning, of replacing everything that had been erased from my memory.

I saw nothing of my family for the next couple of days, but was content in my present industry. Between walks to Jesmond Dene, further trips to look around the little shops, and pleasant conversations with the various nurses, I began writing letters of thanks to the senders of all the get well cards, and avidly rereading Golding's *Lord of the Flies* for my English GCSE, along with an anthology of modern poetry. I was also particularly drawn to my Biology and Chemistry notes, in which I took a hitherto unknown interest. These subjects seemed to have generated in me a sudden and extreme fascination.

After breakfast on Wednesday morning, as I began turning the pages of notes regarding osmosis and homeostasis, Dr Norton came into the room, and as he now commanded the deepest respect from me, I stopped reading and stood up.

'Now James, sit down, won't you,' he said, sitting carefully on the bed. Sheila was with him, smiling and showing her white teeth, her skin clear, her hair raven-black. Dr Norton's eyes looked brighter than usual, which, when I mentioned it, he put down to having had a weekend off.

'You see, when my patients are better, it's better for me, because I can have a rest. Also it was my daughter's wedding down south, so I had a trip down there ... Anyway, how do you feel?' he asked.

I sighed. 'OK. Sometimes I have to read quite slowly and my thoughts get clouded ...'

'Ah, that's just the medication. Eventually we'll jog that down, so don't worry about that. And you're sleeping?'

'Yes, there's no problem there. Hasn't been for a couple of weeks.'

'Good!' For the first time, Dr Norton smiled, whilst obviously meaning it, and slapped both of his own knees, creating a sharp 'click!' sound. He turned to look at Sheila. 'Right! I think we can get him home then, don't you? I think we'd better discharge him.'

'Really?' I said disbelievingly.

'Oh, yes!' said Sheila, glowing, 'he's brilliant now. And he *looks* so well.'

'Yes, that stuff Smythe gave you has really cleared your skin up, hasn't it? But although I'm going to discharge you, I must give a note of caution: you must continue to take your tablets every day. Only then will we be able to jog the medication level down and take you off it. OK?'

'No problem.'

'And do you think you can manage to go back to school? I see you're looking at your schoolbooks there.'

'I think so. It'll be tough, but I've got to do it. I want to take my GCSEs this year – not next year. I don't want to lose any time because of this.'

'Yes, I can understand that. And I have no doubt that you will do it. Your illness is one intrinsically linked with success, not failure. It will provide you with vision and clarity in whatever you do. You're a very clever lad, and I wish you well.'

We shook hands, and Dr Norton simultaneously patted me on the back. 'You know, you've really recovered remarkably quickly for one who was so ill. You had acute mania, which is a very frightening and disorientating thing, but you had the insight to pull through it. And that's the interesting thing about your case. You were like Virginia Woolf, if your friends ask you, touched with fire. She once described herself as, oh, what was it ... Oh, yes, "a porous vessel afloat on sensation".

I think that accurately describes you over the last couple of months, does it not? Ha, ha, ha!'

We laughed for a moment, and then Dr Norton became serious. 'But don't entertain any thoughts of revenge. The important thing is that you are well, that, yes, you were spiked with an unknown substance. But there is nothing that can be done legally with a urine sample. Even though us medics know it's pretty much hard evidence, the law will only accept a blood sample, and that's it. So just be glad you're well, lad.'

'Oh, no. I'm not going to tell a soul.'

'You're a very tough young man coming through this. You're the youngest patient I've had with this illness in thirty-five years of psychiatric practice. Best of luck to you.'

'Thanks for everything you've done, doctor,' I said. Sheila stepped forward to hug me and kissed me on the cheek, and then they left the room.

Punching the air in triumph, I began packing immediately, ecstasy fizzing through my veins and gaining momentum as it sunk in that I was being released, that I was officially sane, that it was over. I pulled all of my clothes out of the wardrobe and flung them on to the bed, opened the suitcase and began packing the underwear, socks, washing things, books, GCSE files, and so on, into the base. And then, in went the shirts and jumpers and jeans, in my fervour placing everything as neatly as I could so that my mother would not need to do too much ironing.

I telephoned my father at work, finding the number on his business card in my black leather wallet.

'I'm coming home, Daddy,' I said.

'Really? For one night or two?' His voice was tuned into business mode: smooth, polished and precise.

'No, forever.' I delighted in the sound of him clearing his throat and his voice beginning to reverberate with excitement.

'Forever? Excellent! I'll see you when I get back!'

And then I telephoned my mother.

'Hi. I've been told you can pick me up now. I can go home.'

'For another night? Oh, you're doing well, aren't you?'

'No, Mummy – forever.'

'Really?!' Her voice lifted into a poignant scream of delight. 'Oh, James, I'm so pleased!' Then there was a pause, a stunned silence as she pulled herself together. I could tell she had begun to cry, and for a moment felt a wave of guilt flood through me as I realised the upset I had caused. But then optimism returned in the form of my mother's voice, which had undergone some urgent rehabilitation. 'Right, I'll come and get you now, darling,'

'Thanks. Oh, one more thing – can you phone up the headmaster and tell him I'd like to see him this lunchtime. And then maybe I could play football on the afternoon during the Games session.'

'Oh, are you sure you're up to it? That's a lot to do in one day.'

'Yes, but I think the sooner I get back to school the better – so does Dr Norton.'

'OK, I'll phone him up, as long as you're sure. I'll drop you off on the way back from Newcastle.'

'Yes, that's what I was thinking.'

In an hour my mother had arrived from the 35 mile drive from Hartlepool, which she had made many times previously to visit me. I was glad she was about to be relieved of that particular burden. Her face was radiant with joy, but creased with the tiredness of recent battles. But the perpetual smile she displayed to the outside world had never receded. I was immensely proud of her courage and will, her refusal to give up. Her constant visits had kept me going, and I felt fortunate to have two parents who truly cared.

Lizzie and Sheila, the duty nurses that day, hugged me and wished me well as I stood by the lift in my jacket, and I thanked them for putting up with me.

'Sorry for being such a loony tune,' I said.

245

'Eeeh, ye were lovely, James. Most of the time. And then at others, well perhaps just a little bit strange ...' said Lizzie. 'But it's a pleasure to see you back to your normal self. Ye've done really well.'

'Thanks, you've all been great. It's been like staying in a hotel. And can you say thanks to Charlotte for me too? She's been great, taking me on so many walks. I really appreciated that. And the night nurses, Peter, Anna and Claire.'

'Oh, we will, don't worry. You get yourself back to school, don't push it, mind you, and I'm sure you'll do well,' said Sheila.

My mother had a few minutes' conversation with them, and in the meantime I went up to see the cleaners Pat and Betsy, who I knew would be taking their eleven o'clock cigarette break.

'Eee, ye goin' home, James? Eee, that's great, isn't it, Betsy?' said Pat, delighted for me. ''Ave a quick tab with us then, for luck!' she said, and I did, and felt the true feeling of freedom beginning to ram home.

Five minutes later, though, as I stepped from the lift, suitcase in hand, and then out the door, filling my lungs with fresh, frosty air, the sun shining warmly down in the midst of a fine spring day, I felt like a man released after two months of prison. I had not suffered the same confinement as a prisoner does, but to be free is to be allowed to govern one's own actions. And that right had now been restored to me, and the shackles removed.

'Does it feel good, James?' asked my mother, 'to be free again?'

'Oh yes!' I said, as I got in the passenger seat and closed the door. I looked up at the hospital exterior, the sun reflecting off the windows, and smiled.

BBC Radio Cleveland's female newsreader announced the time was twelve o'clock. My mother drove the car through the picturesque old high street of Yarm, with its many shops, pubs, and cobbled stones, and turned into the old redbrick side gate of Yarm School.

I was daunted at the sight of boys in their navy school pullovers, running across the driveway to their next lessons so as not to be late, wondering how I was going to get back into all of that. Sixth-formers strolled back from town in groups, smartly dressed in their blazers and sports jackets, eating crisps and sausage rolls and laughing out loud. I was involuntarily shaking with tension, afraid of moving back from the institution of the hospital ward into the traditional institution of school.

'Are you sure you're alright, James? You're sure you can manage this?' my mother asked as she parked the car in the headmaster's car-park, outside the old white three-storey Friarage building, which had been bought twenty-odd years ago and converted into offices and classrooms.

'Yes. I've got to,' I said, forcing the shaking into submission.

I got out of the car and looked around the grounds opposite the Friarage, the stretch of lawn where I had played football every break and lunchtime for the past six years, and beyond this the vast horse chestnut tree. I remembered throwing huge sticks up at it during my first two weeks at the school in order to dislodge conkers, being spotted doing so by a passing Chemistry teacher and dispatched to the headmaster's office. There I'd been given an unexpectedly gentle telling off, as a ten-year-old, in the dark wooden and red leather study with the soundproof door, which had terrified me as I stood outside waiting for him to open it.

I took one final glance at the steep hill and the climbing frame and the small wood that lay beyond it, and gathered myself as my mother fixed her make-up.

But I felt no nervousness now. The shaking had stopped, and I steeled myself for what I was about to say as we entered the front door of the Friarage, turning right on the black and white tiling into the secretary's office, where Neville Tate stood waiting, tall and strongly built, his bald, egg-shaped head looking as if it had been vigorously polished, his blue eyes stern and slightly condescending. His pompous, red leather soundproof door was ajar.

'Well, hello. And how are you both?' he asked, in his nasal, BBC voice.

'Oh, yes, he's fine. I'm sorry we're late by the way. I said half-past eleven, didn't I?' said my mother apologetically.

'It's quite alright. Let's go in, shall we?'

His inquisitive secretary eyed me circumspectly through her small glasses as I passed across the lavish royal blue and white carpet to the open door of the office, returning to her typing as I caught her looking.

The office was the same as it had been six years previously – wood-panelled with a wooden floor and a large, mahogany desk, the room still managing to appear dark despite the presence of three large windows with square panes, two of which looked out on to the memorable horse chestnut, with a further window at the end of the room.

'Do sit down,' he said, as if he were about to conduct an assembly. He evidently knew no other way to communicate than from a position of authority. But I respected him, he somehow commanded respect, and anyway, everything he had said in those assemblies was usually appropriate and insightful.

As we sat on the two red leather chairs, identical to the one on which he sat, my mother cleared her throat, as she always did before saying something important.

'We've come to tell you James is better now.'

'Ah, excellent! Yes, it's been a terrible thing ...' he said, drifting into introspection as though he were remembering what it was like himself, and then came back with the words: 'what was it like, then?' I looked at him and his stern, no-nonsense gaze, and tried to imagine the words I should use to describe an experience so surreal to a man with his feet always placed so firmly within reality.

248

'I can't describe it ... it was sort of – equally light and equally dark. Heaven and hell. To be honest, I don't think you would understand. Anyway, the important thing is, it's over, and I want to do my GCSEs this year, as normal.'

Silence. Both my mother and Mr Tate looked stunned.

'Are you sure?' escaped my mother's voice.

'Don't you think it'd be better to wait till next year, James? That way your grades will be better, the A's you were predicted after the Christmas mocks,' said Neville Tate, wearing his Independent School League Table hat with pride.

'No. I'm going to do them this year,' I said, to all-round disapproval. 'It's my life, and I don't want to lose a year of it. I've wasted two months already.'

'Oh, yes – I quite understand – of course, I ...'

'Thanks,' I said, and smiled.

Moments later, there came a knock at the door.

'Enter!' Mr Tate called out. Harry Welch came in, his broad shoulders slightly slumped with humility, his face serious and his manner mature as always, as he turned to me and shook my hand. His sandy-coloured hair had grown long since I'd last seen him, in a centre parting like my own.

'Hi, Harry!'

'Hi, James, good to see you back,' he said, his blue eyes looking into my own with great sincerity, 'everyone's pleased you're coming back to school.'

'I, erm, spoke to the boys a couple of hours ago at break time, you see, Mrs Fountain. I thought it would be best to let them know he was coming back, and that he was not to be disturbed, you know, since he's only just left the hospital,' said Mr Tate.

'Oh, yes, that's fine,' said my mother. I nodded also, but wasn't so certain that this was a good idea. I wanted everyone to just be as they were. I did not want any special treatment.

'Harry's come to take you to have lunch with your friends, if you'd like to. And then you can take part in the Games session as you wished. How's that?' asked the headmaster.

'Fine!' I said, somewhat shakily. It all seemed so sudden.

But my mother hugged me, thanking Mr Tate as we left the study, and ensured the secretary had her contact details, then took me to the car, opened the boot and lifted out the sports bag, which contained my football boots and kit.

'I'll pick you up at four-thirty, in this car-park, James. There's no need for you to get the bus.'

'OK, Mummy, see you later on.'

Harry led me back into the school. My importance seemed suddenly elevated, I had become a VIP. We walked around the back of the old, partially decrepit Friarage and then through many groups of schoolchildren of all ages, shouting and laughing amongst themselves and running here and there as we passed through the cobbled courtyard. I noticed some curious glances in my direction as we turned away from the brown brick sixth form centre, converted from an old stables years before. To my left I saw familiar teachers walking from the great redbrick classroom block, Mr Thompson, my English teacher, walking briskly towards the dining-hall, but still managing to laugh and joke with several of his army of appreciative pupils *en route*. Mr Crookes was walking in the same direction, wearing his black gown, which meant that he was the 'on duty' teacher this lunchtime, his shoulders bent slightly as if the future of every boy in the school depended on him. Nothing had changed.

And nothing had changed in the dining-hall either, as Harry and I entered it by the teachers' entrance, Harry using my new VIP status to get us past the sixth-former guarding the door so we wouldn't have to queue.

I looked up at the teachers eating on the raised platform to my right, some of whom gazed silently back. As we walked down the aisle between the rows of benches I noticed boys from my year looking at me inquisitively, as well as acquaintances and fellow Hartlepudlians from other years. It felt odd to be a VIP, so I quickly bypassed any potentially embarrassing conversations and walked with Harry towards the food counter, where we each took a tray and selected our food. I decided on fish and chips, with some chocolate sponge for dessert.

We sat down next to Julian Welsh, and I jabbed him in the back. I felt my legs beginning to shake again and worried that someone might notice.

'Jesus!' he said, his blue eyes wide, his face exploding with surprise. 'Jesus, you're back. How the bloody hell are you?'

'My name's not Jesus, it's James. How the bloody hell are you, Ju?'

'Ha ha! Still got the humour, Jim, lad! Nice one. Harry, how ye gettin' on, mate?'

'Good. Fuckin' great to see ye Fred, by the way.'

'And great to see you guys.' Harry had called me Fred ever since the sports teacher Mr Hudson had called me Fred Fountain – supposedly an odd rearrangement of Fred Flintstone – and it had caught on. My hand shook like an alcoholic's as I lifted a glass of water to my lips, and I cowered inwardly at the bemused looks and laughter repaid me. Ben Tillett was somewhere in range to my right, waving his arms, larger than life and sitting with the other members of the rock band he hoped would one day be famous. Other schoolmates I knew less well wished me well as they rose to take back their trays and go outside. And then I clocked him.

There. Strawberry-blond hair, impish, arrogantly-structured round face, staring at me with pale-blue eyes, then looking away quickly and leaving the room, guilty as you like. It was Giles. My hands shook so that my dessert spoon began to tap noisily against the white bowl.

'James, are you alright?' asked Julian, concerned. We were the only ones who remained at our table.

'I'm OK, it's just the medication. Giles Walder plays rugby, doesn't he?' I asked.

251

'Giles? Yeah, I think so. Plays for the Second XV. That still bothering you then? That he stole your girlfriend?'

'No, not at all,' I lied. 'She sent me a card, you know, Rachel. No, that doesn't really bother me any more. But it used to.'

We walked through the school grounds, talking, and at various points I was approached by kids I'd never met, asking me if I was the 'drug boy from the paper', whether I'd really gone to hospital just because I drank two pints of lager, whether alcohol really could make you hallucinate ... But when I shouted at them in frustration they scattered away across the grass like sheep terrified of a barking dog. I was not used to tabloid tittle-tattle.

I had given up rugby two years before, knowing that I was too small and too slow to succeed. I was never much good at football either, but as we got changed, I looked forward to at last having the licence to run around and shake off the nerves created by being back at school.

At the Aisleby playing fields, situated near the opening to Yarm High Street, Mr Ford had me playing right wing at first, after dividing the squad into two teams. But it soon became apparent that my fitness was simply too poor for this. In 15 minutes my body ached and my lungs pleaded for oxygen, and I gave up and went in goal. But I did OK, only letting in a couple of goals, which were decent strikes anyway. But having said that I didn't much care. I was exhausted and wanted the day to be over.

After walking back to school, receiving no questions from my friends about hospitals or drugs, and only those football related – such as the current plight of Leeds United, and why didn't I just give up and support Middlesbrough – I showered and changed and said goodbye, then walked round to the car-park, where my mother's car was already waiting beside a large pine tree.

24

At my mother's recommendation I stayed at home for the remainder of the week, planning to return to school after the Easter holidays. On the following Monday I went into school to meet my English teacher Mr Thompson and my History teacher Mr Crookes, who had kindly taken the time to offer me some advice on how I was to go about completing the required GCSE coursework for both subjects.

'You'll be fine, James,' said Mr Thompson, as he opened a red file and began raking through some essays I'd already completed. As he did so, I gazed around the room and thought of all the hilarious lessons he'd given there, as George Thompson glided through our imaginations using a potent mixture of staff room gossip, controversial views, stunning wit, and a photographic memory for Shakespeare. His mannerisms were more akin to those of a wacky professor than of a school-teacher, and more than once he'd amply demonstrated his ability to recite *Hamlet* purely from memory, capable of running right through a scene from beginning to end whenever prompted. But it was the way in which he taught, his enthusiasm and insightful knowledge of literature that fuelled my own interest, and many others'. Normally Mr Thompson would exude an electric amount of energy, but today his manner was more grave and sedate.

'What is that *shaking*, James? That's not a good sign.'

Dr Norton had only just begun to jog the medication down, and the Chlorpromazine was still causing me to shake slightly.

'It's just the pills I'm on, that's all.'

His eyes gazed large and sceptical from behind his glasses. He wore a white shirt with a dark red tie, grey trousers and a tweed jacket. His short, blackish-grey hair was Brillcreamed back as always with neat Camus-esque slickness, and it occurred to me that he looked not unlike the great French existentialist. And like Camus, he smoked constantly, as he was at that moment, the wrinkles on either side of his fifty-eight-year-old face telling the tale as he savoured the smoke of the third Embassy Light he'd lit since my arrival. I almost asked if I could borrow one, when I realised the interview was at an end.

'There you are,' he said, handing me a sheet of paper with a plan of all I must write to fulfil the coursework requirements. 'And, James, it's a doddle, you could do it blindfold. I've been very worried about you, you know, I'm so pleased you've come through. I'll send you a postcard from Liverpool to see how you're getting on. Got to go and see how mum and dad are – you know how it is. They're both in their eighties, you know.'

'Sure. Thanks a lot for your help.'

'Oh, no problem. And see what you can do about that shaking.'

I smiled and walked out of the door and headed down the long corridor of English classrooms, down the stairs to the History department and turned right into Mr Crookes' classroom, where he was sat at his desk awaiting me.

'Ah, James, hi!' He rested his strong frame upon his elbows, his hands clenched close to his face as if he had been praying. He had begun to grow a goatee beard, as was his sporadic habit, and his brown hair was thick on his head, speckled here and there with minute tinges of white. His eyes were large, brown and wily like those of an owl, magnified by the thick circular glasses he wore. He was more casually dressed than Mr Thompson, in a pair of blue denims, a blue shirt and burgundy jumper.

'Sorry if you've been waiting. Just been to see Mr Thompson,' I said.

'Ah, yes, I can smell the cigarettes! Now – I have some of

your material here – '

He produced some papers with my untidy handwriting upon them in royal blue fountain pen ink, and proceeded to sort through them. As Mr Thompson had done, he listed off a few ideas, and as he did so I wrote them down on my A4 pad. It all seemed quite straightforward what I must do, a couple of essays and other smaller pieces of work, but for the fact that I could remember very little of the history of Nazi Germany. Yet I took comfort in Mr Crookes' assertion that I had the whole four weeks of Easter to complete this in. Maybe reading through it all would jog my memory.

'I think you should be fine. I'm sorry about what happened to you – we all are. But if you can just get this stuff in, it'll set you up nicely for the exams. It'll help you remember the kinds of topics we've covered.'

He spoke carefully and authoritatively as ever, with his deep voice that, like his slightly crouched shoulders, gave an impression that he was consciously fighting an ongoing battle, like the figures in the periods of history he taught.

I thanked my teacher, then went to meet my mother in Strickland & Holt's coffee shop in the centre of Yarm High Street, walking through the doors of the enormous white-washed premises, and then through the gift shop, whose merchandise varied from useful household commodities to objects that can only be described as junk.

Climbing the elaborate wooden staircase to the coffee shop I found my mother sat in a table by the window, looking out at the passing traffic. She turned round suddenly, evidently recognizing my step on the wooden floorboards.

'Hi, James! Did you get everything sorted out?'

'Yeah, they were very helpful,' I said, sitting down, 'they don't think I'll have a problem catching up with the work.'

'Good! That's what you wanted to hear, isn't it? Do you want some tea? I asked for an extra cup for you.'

'Thanks.' She poured the tea, and I dropped in a sugar

255

lump, feeling it slowly diminishing in size beneath the spoon. My hand was shaking again.

'We'll have to phone Dr Norton and see what we can do about that shaking,' my mother said. 'I've got a little surprise for you, by the way. I've booked us all in at the Devonshire Arms at Bolton Abbey for Friday and Saturday night.'

'Great! Oh, I love it there, it's so grand and cosy. But isn't it a bit expensive?'

'Your Grandma wants to treat us all, and she's coming too, with your Aunty Jane. It'll give us all a chance to relax and take in the country air.'

By Friday I had settled in at home, taking the dogs for regular walks, eventually trekking two miles to the nearest shop to buy cigarettes. I painted and read through my school-work, though my powers of concentration were still not good.

The car journey to Skipton was always a visual feast, and on this bright, early spring day it was at its most splendid. Once we had passed Middlesbrough, the moors and woods rolled out before us in an epic display beyond the A19. For thousands of years they had been there, an immovable and imposing backdrop to the life around them, and a protection for those who lived within them. The vivid green of the fields immediately beyond the motorway held cattle and sheep, tiny lambs bleating and calves learning how to moo.

An hour or so later, the Yorkshire Dales brought twists and turns and narrowing roads, my father well used to driving along them, having been brought up in the Skipton area. I marvelled at the blossoming trees, at a wood carpeted with bluebells like something out of a hazy dream, at natural lines of daffodils planted by unwitting birds in wild woodland to my left and right. My sister was sat beside me gazing dreamily through the window, the higher pitches of Madonna's voice making themselves heard through the black headphones of her silver Walkman, held loosely in her hands.

The images of daffodils in the midst of carpets of fallen

brown leaves finally gave way to the opening of The Devonshire Arms Hotel driveway, and the large, grand building constructed some years ago from Yorkshire stone in the traditional farmhouse style. Its grounds sprawled into the distance with the rolling hills and dark woods beyond. Great oaks with outstretched branches lined the distant road, black against the pale grey sky, with glimpses of blue.

After my father parked the car, we took out our cases and walked through the large, cosy bar area with its fire, past the farming implements that adorned the walls, and comfortable couches and chairs. Several old farmers sat on stools by the bar, sipping pints of real ale and reading newspapers, dogs lying loyally at their feet.

I spotted the dartboard and looked forward to having a game with my father, something we always did when we went there. Beside this was a white door which led us into a corridor connecting the bar to the hotel. The hotel had high, ornate cream ceilings and walls. Great oils with impressions of hunting and farming hung from the sides of the reception area, and as I investigated further, I found there was a smart, traditional bar area, and a plush restaurant with a shining grand piano outside it. I could remember coming here for lunch five years before, and how beautiful the food was.

My mother collected the key, and Sooty and Sweep were wagging their tails as they searched excitedly here and there with their noses to the ground, their tiny legs moving quickly to keep up as we turned to go up the wide staircase with its emerald green carpet, and along the corridor to our room.

The family room we found ourselves in was as grand and lavish as the rest of the hotel, with a white bathroom and emerald green carpet, each of the beds covered with a heavy, dark green quilt. By the window shone an ornate mahogany desk.

'You should come and have a swim, James. There's a pool, sauna, and steam room. Victoria and I are going to try it out while your father goes in the bar for a pint.' They were ready to go, and I got off my allotted bed, where I had unintentionally begun to drift off.

'OK, give me a few minutes,' I said, sitting up. 'Actually, I'll just see you down there.'

'Alright then,' said my mother, and off they went with their towels and bathing suits. My father remained behind for a moment.

'You take the key, James,' he said, placing it on my bed, 'and I'll see you in the bar for a Coke and a game of darts when you've finished swimming.'

'Right-o.'

My father smiled and walked out.

Finally alone, I looked out at the view of the Dales through the window, and grabbed my jacket, checking my cigarettes were in the inside pocket, and took a large white towel from the bathroom. Leaving the room, I locked the door and headed down the stairs and out of a side door, and I set off on a pathway that led me round the front of the hotel and along to the health club. On my way, I paused at a simple wooden bench, which was a little damp. Sitting back, I gazed at the green hills and the distant, evergreen woods, dark and mysterious in the late afternoon light. I lit a cigarette and let the smoke swirl slowly from my mouth, listening to the crows cawing raucously, while a skylark sounded panic-stricken as it climbed to an ever-increasing height, the pitch of its call getting higher and higher.

But now I had fallen to earth, and though it was difficult to believe it was over, it was. I contemplated the future like a knight at the end of his quest, pausing for the first time to view the landscape around him, trying to imagine his next step upon the gloriously uncertain trail that is life.